# Introduction to Quality

## Fred Tickle ~~~~~~~~~~, ~~~~~~~~, MIEE, MIQA
## and
## Geoff Vorley MSc, MIQA

Founding Directors of Quality Management & Training Limited
Associate Lecturers at University of Surrey

Fred Tickle

Geoff Vorley

Q
M & T
Quality Management & Training Limited

**Quality Management & Training (Publications) Limited**
PO Box 172 Guildford Surrey United Kingdom GU2 7FN
**Telephone:** +44 (0) 1256 358083 or +44 (0) 1483 453511 **Fax:** +44 (0) 1483 453512
**E-mail**: help@qmt.co.uk **Website**: www.qmt.co.uk

**Quality Management & Training (Publications) Limited**
PO Box 172 Guildford Surrey GU2 7FN


First Published by Quality Management & Training (Publications) Limited 1998
Reprinted by Quality Management & Training (Publications) Limited March 1999 - with addendum
Second edition by Quality Management & Training (Publications) Limited 2000
Third edition by Quality Management & Training (Publications) Limited 2002

**British Library Cataloguing in publications data**

A catalogue record for this book is available from the British Library


**ISBN   1-904302-00-9**


Printed and Bound in Great Britain by :
Biddles Limited
Woodbridge Park Estate, Woodbridge Road, Guildford, Surrey GU1 1DA

**Table of Contents**

# Table of Contents

# Synopsis

## Introduction to the Book

The aim of this book is to provide a clear and comprehensive understanding of the principles of quality assurance. The book will explain the way in which these quality assurance principles relate and can be applied to the design, development, manufacture and delivery of products and services. The object is to enhance the reader's awareness of Quality Assurance, its terminology and bring the subject alive sufficiently to encourage and motivate for quality assurance. Since statistical methods play a vital part in any Quality Assurance or Total Quality Management initiatives, it is for this reason a practical approach has been adopted in the explanation of this important topic. Information is provided by practical examples of the application of statistics in the quality environment.

The book covers the Institute of Quality Assurance (IQA) D1 syllabus and is of obvious application for students participating in the IQA D1 examination. As a result of adhering to the requirements of the IQA D1 syllabus, the book's content reflects the current thinking of the IQA, in terms of the latest key quality issues facing Directors, Managers and Technicians. The book provides a clear approach and examples of how to respond to these key quality issues.

Introduction to Quality is part of the Quality Management series of books which includes: Quality Management (Principles and Practice), Quality Management (Tools & Techniques), Quality Management (Communications and Projects) and Quality Management (Information Technology). For clarity and continuity purposes, there is correctly some overlap between these titles. However, this book is expected to be a "stand alone", comprehensive and practical reference to introduction to quality.

The book is divided into seven parts. Below is an outline of the contents of each section and what could be reasonably expected to be appreciated, having studied each section.

# Introduction to Quality

## Part 1: Quality Concepts, Philosophy and Systems
This section is intended to provide sufficient information to:
- understand the concepts of quality, its control and various definitions associated with quality and reliability,
- establish and interpret company quality policy,
- understand natural, material and subjective standards and their applicability,
- develop and create a calibration system,
- understand the concepts of traceability and hierarchy in connection with inspection and testing measuring equipment,
- understand the relationship between specifications, measurements and process capabilities,
- understand various quality control strategies applicable to different organisational structures and processes; volume, flow, batch, service, etc.
- prepare quality control schemes and their documentation,
- control specification amendment and implement a concession procedure.

## Part 2: Standardising Organisations
This section is intended to provide sufficient information to:
- describe the roles and responsibilities of the various standardising organisations (company, industrial, national and international) and the importance of international standards harmonisation,
- understand and complete the process or procedure for obtaining product certification including a third party,
- describe the need, importance and application of specifications and standardisation in the quality control system,
- prepare specifications for the purposes of testing a product or service,
- use a product or service specification as a basis for a contract or conducting an external audit,
- determine from the product or service specification the process measurement criteria.

## Part 3: Total Involvement Quality
This section is intended to provide sufficient information to:
- understand the concept of total involvement in quality assurance and importance of communication and feedback of information,
- justify quality assurance activities with regard to commercial, legal responsibilities and cost reduction,
- control the process of procuring bought-in goods and services,
- complete a supplier evaluation and vendor rating,
- organise and document purchasing and sub-contracting procedures,
- understand how suppliers' performance is measured.

## Part 4: Quality Costs
This section is intended to provide sufficient information to:
o       explain how the quality department can make a major contribution to the profitability of an organisation,
o       complete a quality cost analysis using the
  •           prevention, appraisal and failure costs model
  •           process cost model
  •           loss function.

## Part 5: Statistical Process Control
This section is intended to provide sufficient information to:
o       use process capability analysis to determine the ability of the process to meet the quality requirements,
o       understand the basic ideas of control charts and compile control charts for variables and attributes,
o       calculate and use decision lines on control charts.
o       use and application of control charts both variable and attribute.

## Part 6: Reliability
This section is intended to provide sufficient information to:
o       be able to define reliability, with specific regard to ISO 8402/BS 4778,
o       interpret lifetime distributions in terms of probability density function and reliability function,
o       understand the basic concepts of simple series and parallel systems and the use of redundancy to improve reliability,
o       understand the principles of reliability testing and reliability programme management.

## Part 7: Variability
This section is intended to provide sufficient information to:
o       determine the ability of the process to meet specification,
o       understand the concept of variability when applied to continuous and discrete random variables,
o       calculate normal, binomial and poisson distributions,
o       apply acceptance sampling by attributes,
o       construct operating characteristics curves for single sampling plans,
o       interpret the implications of an operating characteristic curve and determine the risks involved in sampling,
o       construct probability distributions for continuous random variables.
o       understand the properties of the normal distribution and explain the reasons for its widespread use to model production and service processes,

6

○        understand how to complete an analysis of tolerance requirements and a statistical analysis of tolerancing,

○        understand, calculate and apply cusum charts.

*The book was intended to be written in a way that hopefully makes the various techniques and approaches to Quality Assurance self explanatory. However, if the reader has any problems with the contents or has a quality problem or issues that they would like to discuss further, please do not hesitate to contact Fred or Geoff. We can be contacted via the publishers - **we welcome the opportunity to discuss quality issues**.*

This book could not have been completed without the invaluable contribution provided by Edda Saunders BSc (Hons) and Denise Grant BA (Hons).

# Part 1

# Quality Concepts, Philosophy and Systems

# Introduction to Quality

## Quality Concepts, Philosophy and Systems

### The Quality Concept

*Quality is the totality of features and characteristics of a product or service that bear on its ability to satisfy a given need (BS 4778/ISO 8402).*
*Degree to which a set of inherent characteristics fulfils requirements (ISO 900)*

When asked to name a quality pen most people respond with names such as Parker, Schaefer, Mont Blanc, Cross or Waterman. Occasionally, someone suggests Bic. This obvious contrast reveals misconceptions about the word 'quality'. I am sure that the quality manager of Bic would consider that his pens are of high quality just as much as those of other manufacturers. There is clearly a difference between, say, a Parker pen and a Bic pen but it is not quality. In simple terms, quality means Fitness for Purpose or, 'to satisfy a given need'.

Compare the expectations for a Bic pen with those for a Parker and it can be seen that they serve different purposes. The Bic pen is considered to be merely a writing tool while the Parker pen is expected to serve the additional purpose of being a prestigious gift. Consequently, the Parker pen will have many more features and characteristics to satisfy its purpose.

Needs cover more than mere function. Many factors affect the ability of a product or service to satisfy needs. Needs include:
- availability
- appearance
- method of distribution
- initial cost
- running costs
- user awareness or knowledge
- other possible uses including reasonable misuse (e.g. using a screw driver to open a tin of paint or a chair to stand on)
- expected life
- storage requirements
- service requirements
- interaction with other items when used
- whether it is user friendly

Needs also must include what the product must not do:

- o      bombs must not explode until required to do so
- o      products must not cause:
  - •      injury
  - •      a threat to health
  - •      a safety hazard
  - •      damage to the environment
- o      and they must not do this:
  - •      when they are working
  - •      when they are not working
  - •      when they are being repaired or serviced
  - •      when they fail
  - •      when they are being disposed of

## Quality versus Grade

*Grade is category or rank given to the different quality requirements for objects having the same functional use (ISO 9000).*

Quality is the degree to which the customers' expectations are met. If the Bic pen meets all of its expectations then it is of a high quality. Similarly, a Parker pen which did not meet all of its expectations would be a low quality pen. Quality is, therefore, independent of price; it is related to expectations.

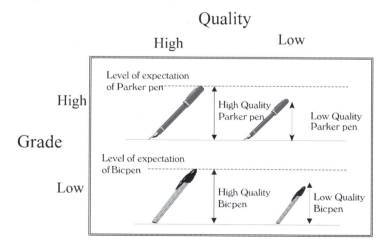

**Figure 1** Quality versus Grade

# Introduction to Quality

As stated above, there is clearly a difference but it is not quality. ISO 8402 defines this difference in expectations as the GRADE of the product or service.

Quality should not be confused with grade. Grade is the extent of features and characteristics offered for a given price. Grade is a function of price. A higher grade demands a higher price. Consumers choose the grade according to their pocket coupled with their expectations. Quality, on the other hand, is not a function of price. Consumers expect a high quality regardless of what they have paid - the product must satisfy their expectations.

The above distinction is particularly important in these days when public services are being contracted out. As the cost of public services becomes more competitive, there is a great danger that the lowering of quality can become confused with the lowering of grade. Traditionally in the UK, public services have evolved almost regardless of cost and, therefore, many features of services have become the expected norm. When the cost of these services has to be directly paid for, as opposed to a voted budget, questions are asked as to what is being paid for. This may lead to the pruning of services down to essential features. This should not be confused with the quality, which should still be of the highest standard for the grade.

By way of illustration: eye surgery in the UK is still carried out in high grade, and consequently expensive, operating theatres. In Russia, a large proportion of eye surgery is now carried out on a bus equipped with the minimum essential facilities without compromising the quality of the surgery.

This trend is likely to increase, so it is vitally important that to avoid 'throwing out the baby with the bath water' a clear distinction is made between quality and grade.

Craftsmen and scientists have long traditions of producing the best that is possible regardless of cost. It is necessary to learn what it means to produce the best that is possible, albeit with reduced expectations as to the scope of features included in the product or service within a price constraint.

Is it really the role of the hospital to provide staff with a bowling green and immaculate cricket pitch employing teams of groundsmen and gardeners? Patients are increasingly asking "what am I paying for?". These are emotive issues with political overtones which must not  cloud over judgement when the customers decide what they are prepared to pay for and  the price they are prepared to pay for it.

# Quality Concepts, Philosophy and Systems

## Customers, Products, Materials and Service

It is not always obvious who the customer is, what the product is or what material is being processed.

Product is defined as the result of activities or processes. A product may include service, hardware, processed materials or software. A product can be tangible (assemblies or processed material) or intangible (knowledge or concepts).

Material is what is processed. Material may be physical or virtual (information).

For example, for an estate agent, although commission is paid by the seller the buyer is nevertheless a customer. The product is a service (advisor, negotiator) to both the buyer and seller. The material is the information which the estate agent processes.

## Quality of a Product (physical)

The following diagram illustrates the relationship of various quality related terms:

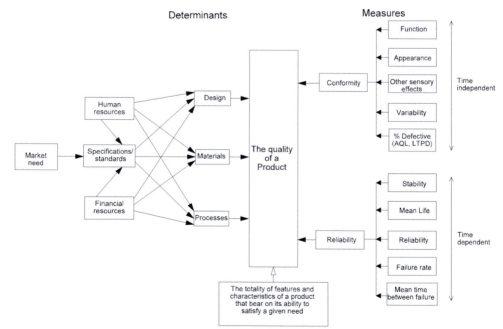

**Figure 2** Definition of the Quality of a Product

## Introduction to Quality

Note: There are two measures of quality: conformity and reliability.

*Conformity* is determined by inspection and test - the 'as-made' condition.

*Reliability* is the probability of what happens in time under defined conditions and is indicated by the mean time between failure (MTBF), failure rate, or probability of successful operation, etc.

# Quality Concepts, Philosophy and Systems

## Quality of Service

What distinguishes service product from physical product is the inseparability of the delivery process from the content. In other words, since the delivery of a service is often face to face with a customer, any error in the service is immediately evident to the customer with no time to take corrective action.

Where there is continuous customer interface during delivery, i.e. services, there are two parallel processes to consider:

a)      what is being delivered and
b)      the delivery process itself.

Service measures may be qualitative (soft standards) as well as quantitative (hard standards):

- facilities, capacity, resources/availability
- waiting time, delivery time, process time
- hygiene, safety, reliability, security
- responsiveness, accessibility, courtesy, comfort, aesthetics of environment, competence, dependability, accuracy, completeness, state of the art, credibility, effectiveness of communication.

Hard standards are objectively verifiable, i.e. they can be measured directly in units such as time, size, light or sound levels, accuracy (compliance to specification) etc.

Soft standards, being subjective, may be measured using questionnaires with scales such as those used by restaurants and airlines to gather customer opinion about their service.

For example: attitudes of server, appearance, helpfulness, empathy, advice/counsel etc.

# Introduction to Quality

## The Determinants of Quality

*Quality of Design*
This is the degree to which the user's needs have been understood, translated into product or service specifications and communicated to subsequent departments. Marketing, sales or contract departments are usually responsible for ensuring that the user's needs are fully understood.

- While Clive Sinclair's C5 car was extremely well researched and designed, customer reaction was not tested prior to its launch and this caused disastrous results.
- Currently, corned beef tins cause 11,500 reported casualties, who have been cut by tins, per year in the UK. Design departments are responsible for verifying the soundness of designs.
- When modifying the design of the Chinook helicopter propeller drive by increasing the size of a bolt, designers neglected to examine adequately the consequences of the reduced wall thickness caused by the increased hole size, again with disastrous results.

Drawing offices are responsible for communicating design specifications in an unambiguous way. Drawings which specified that a two-part assembly should be tested to withstand 40N force did not specify a tolerance, with the result that the inspector applied 60N force "to be on the safe side" thus causing a potential weakness which may not have been discovered until some time after delivery.

*Design Control* includes the planning, techniques and documented procedures used to ensure that the customer's requirements are fully understood and interpreted into a practical and viable manufacturing specification, with due consideration for all performance, safety and reliability related requirements.

### *Quality of Procurement*
Purchasing and quality departments should be responsible for ensuring that the required quality is obtained for materials, components and sub-contract services, which they are effectively purchasing on behalf of the customer. Many companies have suffered losses because they have "been let down by their suppliers". Companies cannot pass on the responsibility to their sub-contractors or suppliers. What they can do is to carry out sufficient assessments of suppliers to establish what confidence they can have with regard to the quality of their supplies or services before purchasing from them. For example, during 1987, the US government had to set up a senate enquiry into the extent of the potential risk resulting from the importation of nuts and bolts from

unknown sources in the Far East; it was discovered that mild steel was being supplied as high strength alloy steel.

*Purchasing Control* includes all the techniques associated with ensuring that the quality of supplies consistently meet the specified requirements in terms of price, performance, delivery, service and quality.


## Quality of Processes

The quality of processes starts with planning. Clearly, the method of manufacture must be economic but it is false economy, for instance, to leave inspection to the last stage, which very often happens. It is usually going to cost more in the long run to correct any defects found at this stage. Starting a job without checking first of all that everything necessary to do the job is available, appears to be stating the obvious, but it is amazing how often this is the case. Using the wrong tools or make-do gauges, not checking the first-off, not monitoring the process for drift or deterioration of tool condition, taking short cuts, relying on instruments and controllers which have not been calibrated, mishandling, poor storage facilities are just some of the common causes of poor quality. For example, in 1989 signals at Clapham Junction (Britain's busiest railway junction) malfunctioned, resulting in many deaths and injuries, because a disconnected wire was not trimmed back or made secure during modifications.

*Process Control* includes all the documented methods associated with ensuring that the product conforms to specified requirements, including the subsequent stages, such as: packaging, installation and servicing.

**Quality Control**

*The traditional approach towards quality (detection)*

In the days when a craftsman saw the whole job through from start to finish, quality was synonymous with craftsmanship. The craftsman would ensure quality at every stage. The principles of Taylorism[1], Fordism and work study led to the division of labour. First of all between 'Planners' and 'Doers' and, secondly, between the tasks themselves. De-skilling led, on the one hand, to a loss of personal involvement and a sense of pride in one's work, and a need for planning and co-ordination on the other. This resulted in the formation of centralised inspection departments and quality being controlled by filtering out defective work during inspection stages. It was reactive and detection orientated. It also tended to suggest that quality problems were related to the manufacturing process, whereas studies on the origin of quality problems have shown that up to 60% of quality problems are design faults. If the traditional approach to controlling quality, with the its emphasis on monitoring the manufacturing or production process is employed, then if there is a design error, the best that can be achieved is - to make the product perfectly wrong! Clearly, there was a need to extend the control of quality into other areas that could have an impact on the final quality of the product or service.

---

[1]      See page 23

# Traditional Inspection

### Detection Oriented

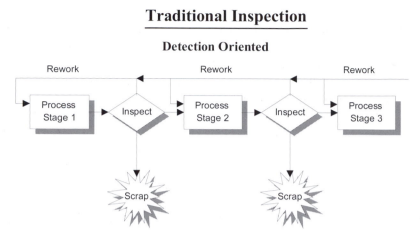

Inspection is used as a filter to sort good from bad
Continuous feedback of defective work for correction

**Figure 3** Traditional inspection approach

In the figure above the procedure for each stage is:

Step 1    Set up machine

Step 2    Inspect first off

Step 3    If first off is OK then continue, otherwise re-set the machine until OK

Step 4    On completion, transport goods to the inspection department to carry out 100% inspection to sort the good from the bad

Step 5    Scrap or re-work defectives.

There are a number of problems with this approach:

o    Time, effort and energy are wasted on manufacturing defective products

o    Loss of manufacturing capacity carrying out re-work

o    Delivery delays and loss of profit or custom

o    100% inspection does not necessarily mean 100% detection and, therefore, some defectives find their way to the customer.

---

**Traditional inspection = DETECTION of out-of-limit parts = Waste**

---

# Introduction to Quality

## The modern approach towards quality (prevention)

The complexities in technology and integration of designs have made total quality control by inspection alone unsuitable. Inspection can only determine the quality of an item in the 'as-made' condition. To ensure reliability, which is the time-dependent dimension of quality, it is necessary to build-in quality at every stage. In recent years a new approach towards achieving quality and reliability has evolved known as the systems approach to Quality Assurance. Since every stage of the product or service cycle is a potential source of failure, it must be considered just what could go wrong at each stage. Quality is the degree to which this is successfully achieved for each of the above functions. It follows, therefore, that quality achievement must be planned. This implies the examination at each stage of the process and careful consideration of the potential deviations and the methods and techniques necessary to prevent the occurrence of defective work. Quality Assurance is pro-active rather than re-active.

## Quality Control Approach

### Prevention Orientated

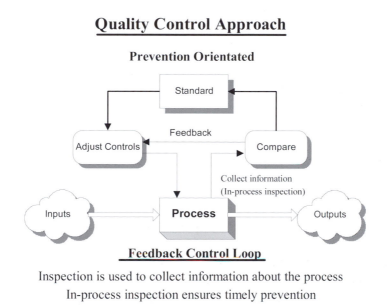

Feedback Control Loop

Inspection is used to collect information about the process
In-process inspection ensures timely prevention

**Figure 4** Preventive approach to Quality Control

# Quality Concepts, Philosophy and Systems

## Step 1. Start right

o      Check that the operator, machine, tools etc. are capable with respect to the specified tolerance

o      Check instructions, drawings, documentation are available and at the right issue

o      Set up the machine

o      Inspect first off

o      If the first off is not within tolerance readjust machine and repeat until correct.

## Step 2. Keep right

o      Inspect samples at suitable intervals

o      Plot inspection results on control charts

o      Interpret control chart and take corrective action when necessary.

## Step 3. Finish right

o      Inspect last item and plot on chart

o      Complete records and return documentation

o      Protect components for transport to next stage

o      Return tools for refurbishment and safe storage

o      Carry out any planned maintenance.

## Benefits of this approach:

o      Manufacture of defective items is avoided

o      Defective work is prevented and, therefore, does not result in field failures

o      Increased manufacturing efficiency and profitability.

---

**Modern Techniques    = PREVENTION of out-of limit parts**
**= Savings/Benefits**

---

It is clearly more sensible to avoid waste and hold-ups by adopting a policy of **PREVENTION** and **"Right First Time"**.

# Introduction to Quality

## Total Quality Control - A. V. Feigenbaum

Feigenbaum is one of the quality experts who helped the Japanese to understand and implement Quality Control techniques in the 1950s. Feigenbaum's book "Total Quality Control" was originally written in 1951 but organisations in the West are only now employing some of the concepts and principles embodied in his book. Total Quality Control, not to be confused with Total Quality Management (TQM), may be considered to be the forerunner to ISO 9001 (1994). Feigenbaum's book is essentially a model for a Quality Management System (like ISO 9000) rather than TQM which may be considered more of a motivational concept. Originally, quality assurance was mainly considered to be controlling the quality of manufacture. Feigenbaum had the foresight to see that this was only part of the story. Quality was to be applied to the total process and needed to involve all functions associated with the process of fulfilling the customer requirements; from initial specification and design control through to the manufacturing stages. More recently, this concept has been extended vertically into service industries and, horizontally, by encompassing all departments within an organisation, with the introduction of the concept of 'internal customers'.

One of the key elements of Feigenbaum's Total Quality Control message is the need for a co-ordinated and documented approach to controlling quality across the complete organisation. These documented procedures are the guide for the action of personnel throughout all of the process stages of delivering a product or service. The Total Quality Control approach to each of these process stages is shown in the diagram and explained below.

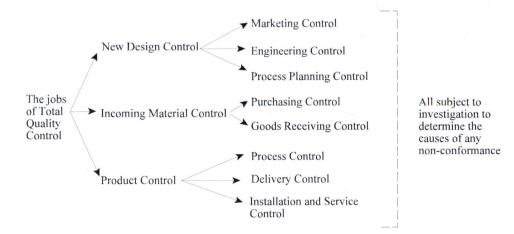

**Figure 5** Feigenbaum's Total Quality Control

*Quality Assurance Model*

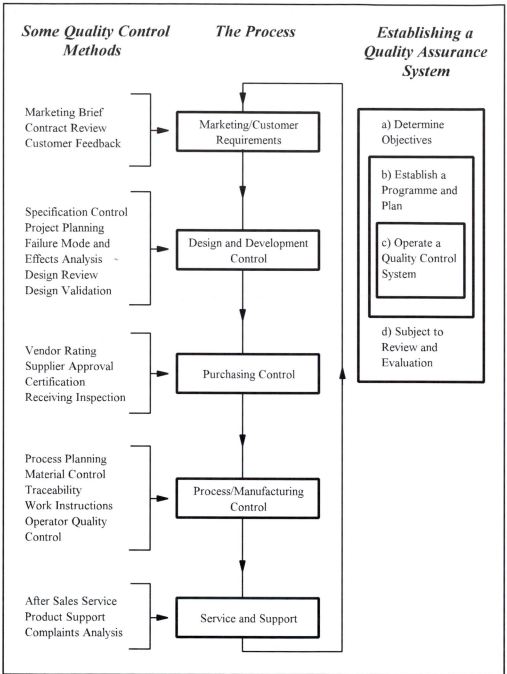

**Figure 6** Quality Assurance Model. Adapted from BS4891

**Figure 6** describes a typical process from customer requirements, through design and development, purchase of materials, process control to delivery and subsequent service support.

The Quality Assurance system has in this case established the support activities that ensure that quality control activities are consistently and effectively implemented.

The right-hand side of the diagram indicates the process of determining the quality system for each stage in the process.

The left-hand side of the diagram indicates some of the quality control methods that would be appropriate for regulating each stage. For example, at the design and development stage the quality control objectives include implementation of specification control, project planning, the application of design techniques such as Failure Mode Effect Analysis (FMECA), design review and design validation. The list is not complete. There are numerous other quality control methods that can be employed.

a)      Determine objectives: specify what is to be achieved.
b)      Establish a programme and plan how these objectives are to be achieved.
c)      Operate a quality control system for each stage in the process.
d)      Review and evaluate the implementation of the applied quality controls by continuous monitoring of the system through reviews and audits.


**Quality Assurance**

*Taylorism and Fordism*

As already stated, up to the end of the nineteenth century, quality was determined by craftsmanship. Long apprenticeships ensured that skills were passed on from generation to generation. Often, craftsmen would see the whole job through from start to finish. Management had little to do with the content or method of working.

During the early part of the twentieth century, Frederick Winslow Taylor and Henry Ford set out to increase productivity, to minimise human error and variation by dividing the *planning* of work from the *doing* of work. Planning was to be the responsibility of management specialists trained in the techniques of method study and work measurement. By transferring skills to machines and reducing workers to mere doers who were not expected to think about the way things were to be done, it was possible to employ unskilled labour which was plentiful at that time, owing to the rapid increase in immigrants from Europe and migrants from the country. Further separation of the responsibility for quality by the centralisation of inspection left the average worker bereft of any personal involvement in the work. As a consequence, workers become increasingly mercenary about work seeking financial compensation for the sheer monotony and boredom they experience in the workplace.

*Job Satisfaction*

This trend came to a head in the 1960s, particularly in the car industry. Furthermore, there was increasing evidence that this policy of treating workers as unthinking machine operators, combined with the effect that this had on their attitudes, played a significant part in poor quality. Many schemes were devised in an attempt to counter these negative attitudes at work and increase job involvement. Schemes such as Job Awareness, Job Rotation, Job Enlargement and Job Enrichment were collectively known as Job Satisfaction schemes or Job Restructuring.

*Japan*

Meanwhile, Japan was being guided through a rapid transition from its non-threatening pre-industrial status to a threatening contender in the world market place, by the Quality experts Deming, Juran and Feigenbaum. However, having the benefit of hindsight, the Japanese avoided the extremes of Taylorism and Fordism. Instead they engaged the participation of the workers in the form of Quality Circles. By allowing small groups of workers to have regular meetings to learn how to solve problems, they discovered enormous achievements could be made in the form of savings and quality improvements.

**Quality Assurance today**

Quality Assurance is about everyone being responsible for quality. It is an about-turn on the Fordist perception of the worker. The last 30 years have seen a new philosophy of management emerging in which the worker is seen as a key problem solver and management as the resource. The current buzz word is 'empowerment'. Many middle managers see this as a threat to their authority and power. This is due to a misconception of the idea. Empowerment should not be seen as a diminishing of management's power but an unleashing of the worker's latent creative power hitherto denied.

# Introduction to Quality

According to traditional views of economics, countries which have the most material resources would lead world markets. That is why so many wars have been fought over resource rich countries. It explains why pioneers were financed to extend the British Empire. It explains the concept of the Commonwealth. However, the Japanese at the end of the war, left with no natural resources, demonstrated the truth of the most valuable asset, which the West had denied. This was to recognise the potential of each individual human being. The traditional views have been challenged by this new approach and found wanting. We are now having to learn from the Japanese as to how to undo a century of non-involvement of workers.

The most common approach is the establishment of teams and the organisational adjustments necessary to develop teamwork. Workers are now being involved at all levels of decision-making in the organisation. Taylor's division of labour at the start of this century introduced the need for formal communication between the 'planners' and the 'doers'. At the start of this millennium as we have moved beyond the industrial age into the information age, new communication skills are needed to allow the full participation of all staff while maintaining co-ordination and control. Accountability is being decentralised enabling local involvement in the decision-making process. At the same time, everyone is perceived as part of an information loop known as the *feedback* system. For example, the role of inspection is no longer to detect defective work but to gather information about the process with a view to preventing defective work.

One thing is sure, competent and committed leadership is more important than ever. Managers can no longer separate their own behaviour from what they expect from others and that is why schemes such as ISO 9000 place so much emphasis on the Quality Policy Statement. Managers must be seen to 'walk the talk'.

# A Documented Quality System

## Quality Policy and the Documented Quality System

A Quality System is the organisational structure, responsibilities, procedures, processes and resources for implementing quality management. The quality system should only be as comprehensive as needed to meet the quality objectives. For contractual, mandatory and assessment purposes, demonstration of the implementation of identified elements in the system may be required.

### *An example of the importance of quality records - The USS Thresher*

The accuracy of this story may not be exactly correct but it does convey the importance of quality systems and records.

The USS Thresher was an American nuclear submarine which sank with the loss of all crew. As a result there was a formal inquiry held to identify the possible causes of the disaster. The inquiry team comprised of (amongst others) the people responsible for what is now known as first level systems. i.e. those systems concerned with preventing submerging and surfacing of the submarine.

- o        The propulsion system (propellers, steam turbines etc.)
- o        Ballast system (pumps and air and hydraulics etc.)
- o        The control surfaces (rudder,  hydroplanes, etc.)
- o        The power supply (nuclear power plant)
- o        Pressure hull (structure of the submarine)

The story goes that the Naval Officers associated with each of the above elements had assembled when Admiral Rickover walked in with a huge pile of records. "Good day gentlemen" he said " I have here all the quality records associated with the Threshers Nuclear power plant proving that my Nuclear system works satisfactorily.  Where are your records to prove the same?" With that said, the Admiral walked out of the room. The truth  of the above may be in doubt (but the point has still been well made i.e. that the Nuclear Quality Management System was in place). Unfortunately the same rigeur was not in place for the submarine's other system (e.g. the engines).   The other officers could not prove (provide quality records) the quality of their systems.  From this incident "First Level" was born.  From this time onwards all systems which effect the submarines' ability to submerge and surface were classified as First Level and therefore attract a higher standard of control (A Quality System Standard).

# Introduction to Quality

## *Demonstration and documentation*

Demonstration of the quality system refers to:

- the adequacy of the quality system (e.g. in design, production, installation and servicing)
- providing documented evidence that the prescribed system is operating effectively.

Documentation may include quality manuals, descriptions of quality related procedures, quality system auditing reports and other quality records. All documentation should be legible, dated (or status), clear, readily identifiable and maintained in an orderly manner.

Data may be hard-copy or stored electronically in a computer. In addition, the quality management system should provide a method for removing and/or disposing of documentation used in the manufacture of products when that documentation has become out of date. The following are examples of the types of documents requiring control:
- drawings
- specifications
- inspection instructions
- test procedures
- work instructions
- operation sheets
- quality manual
- operational procedures
- quality assurance procedures.

The system should also require that sufficient records be maintained to demonstrate achievement of the required quality and verify effective operation of the quality management system. The following are examples of quality records requiring control:
- contract or order reviews
- list of suppliers and subcontractors
- inspection reports
- test data
- certificates of conformity
- audit reports
- calibration data
- customer complaints
- training.

# A Documented Quality System

Quality records should be retained for a specified period, in such a manner as to be retrievable for analysis in order to identify quality trends and the need for, and effectiveness of, corrective action. Whilst in storage, quality records should be protected from damage, loss and deterioration due to environmental conditions.

## *Quality system documentation structure*

The Quality System documentation is usually structured into three levels as follows:

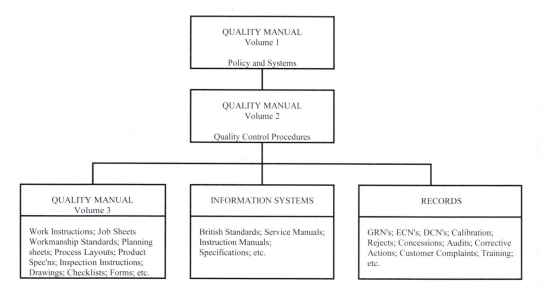

Volume 1 of the Quality Manual provides an overview of the Company's Quality System and the Company's policy with respect to the requirements of ISO 9001.

Volume 2 of the Quality Manual provides a more detailed description of the overall procedures and responsibilities for operating the Quality System.

The documentation at level three is divided into three:
a) Volume 3 - documentation which is specific to customers orders and instructs employees on the correct sequence to perform various tasks.
b) Information Systems - general information and data such as specifications and standards.
c) Records - records which demonstrate the operation of the quality system and provide the basis for analysis and corrective actions.

# Introduction to Quality

*Management commitment - The quality policy statement*

The Quality Policy Statement is a company's statement of intent with regard to the quality of the goods or services provided to their customers. This statement is usually found in the front of the Quality Manual and posted throughout the company.

*Purpose of the quality policy statement*

- o To provide the customer with the confidence that the company is going to supply good products or services and that they have made a commitment to quality
- o To indicate to the employees that the company's management has given the 'stamp of authority' to the commitment to quality.

*Contents of quality policy statement*

Quality Policy Statements are often found to contain the following:

- o Reference to satisfying the customer's requirements
- o Reference to the commitment to effective management and cost effective products or services
- o Statement that compliance with the contents of the Quality Manual and associated procedures is a mandatory requirement on all employees
- o Signature at the end of the policy statement by the chief executive of the company endorsing the commitment.

QUALITY POLICY STATEMENT

Quality Management and Training Limited is proud of its reputation for providing consultancy and training services in the field of quality assurance. To ensure that this reputation continues and that clients can remain confident of the quality of our service, we have implemented management systems which meet the requirements of ISO 9001.

To this end, all activities affecting the processes of consultancy and training are controlled by procedures which are defined in a Quality Manual. These procedures, while not restricting the flair and experience of the consultants, ensure that essential tasks are controlled and checked for accuracy.

It is, therefore, a requirement on all personnel in the organisation to comply with the procedures laid down in the Quality Manual and the associated work instructions which are issued with my full approval and commitment.

(Signed)
*Fred Tickle*   2 June 2002
Managing Director.

*Interpreting the Quality Policy Statement*

No matter how well intentioned, it is easy for a Quality Policy Statement to become fine words without any real effect on how the company operates and without it being possible to check whether it is being fulfilled. It is essential, therefore, that the company makes it quite clear how the Quality Policy Statement is to be interpreted. This can take various forms:

- The statement often needs to be translated into language which is more appropriate for the local work - a production line, a purchasing office, a design group, and so on
- ISO 9001 requires companies to translate the quality policy into specific objectives. This allows the company to check how well its policy is being realised more exactly
- Review by management at board meetings.

## The Quality Hierarchy

*Quality Assurance:* All those planned and systematic actions necessary to provide adequate confidence that a product or service will satisfy given requirements for quality.

*Quality Control:* The operational techniques and activities that are used to fulfil requirements for quality.

*Inspection:* Activities such as measuring, examining, testing, gauging one or more characteristics of a product or service and comparing these with specified requirements to determine conformity.

**Table 1** The Quality Hierarchy

**Quality Assurance**

The activities and functions concerned with the attainment of quality.

**Quality Control**

The operational techniques and activities that sustain the product/service requirements.

**Inspection**

Inspection is the process of measuring, examining, testing, gauging or otherwise comparing the item with the applicable requirements.

# Standards and Specifications

## Natural, Material and Subjective Standards and Specifications

### Introduction

Standards and specifications are playing an increasingly larger role in modern business. This is happening for many reasons, for example:

- Formal contracts are becoming more and more important, and a formal definition of the goods and services required is an integral part of this
- Requirements are becoming more and more complex, and documented definitions are essential for proper understanding and agreement as to what the requirement actually is
- Work teams are becoming larger and more complex too, so standards and specifications are essential to communication.

### Definitions - General

Standard            -            **the ideal**; a model, a level of quality to which others must conform

Specification       -            **the description**; to state definitely, to give details of, to indicate precisely

Code of Practice    -            **the method**; details of what is practicable

*Objective standards - also referred to as hard standards*
- something tangible against which to compare your work
- existing independently of perception
- a material standard as opposed to a concept or idea
- undistorted by emotion or personal bias, e.g. gauge blocks; standard cell; noise level with decibel metre.

*Subjective standards - also referred to as soft standards*
- related to people's perception of what something might be
- something perceived
- standard based on a person's idea of what it ought to be e.g. noise level guessed at by a person; colour matching.

# Introduction to Quality

## British Standards Definitions

### Standard (from BS 0 Part 1 - 1981)

A standard is a technical specification or other document available to the public, drawn up with the co-operation and consensus or general approval of all interests affected by it, based on the consolidated results of science, technology and experience. It is aimed at the promotion of optimum community benefits and approved by a body recognised on the national, regional or international level.

### Specification

The specification is the document that prescribes in detail the requirements with which the product or service has to comply.

"A specification is essentially a means of communicating the needs or intentions of one party to another".

The specification details the standard, although a specification need not have anything to do with a standard, i.e. it may be details of a 'one off'.

### Codes of practice

Codes of practice should recommend good accepted practice as followed by competent practitioners  (BS 0 Part 3).

NOTE:  A code of practice is a recommendation only!

# Standards and Specifications

## Product Specifications

A specification operates by naming explicitly and mentioning definitely the details of some projected work.

Key words in specification writing are *explicitly* and *definitely* and if it is to be any good, must be *unambiguous*. The specification is the document which describes and sets the standard of materials and workmanship. If it is ambiguous or loosely worded no one will know the standards they are expected to achieve.

The *aim* then of a specification is to state in words and phrases using drawings and diagrams, where relevant, the standard of work and quality required.

The specification is a means of communicating ideas from one person to another.

What is intended to happen? This is the question the *product designer* asks himself, hence from his ruminations a *design specification* is achieved. To make certain his wishes have been carried out an *acceptance test specification* is written and followed.

For new products there will be feedback to the designer from R&D (Research and Development), and other engineers enabling him to take corrective action, where necessary, to ensure everyone's objectives have satisfactorily been met, i.e. the quality element 'Fit for Purpose'.

For large orders, or an order of a specific nature, such as a missile system or a nuclear power plant, the *customer* may write his own specification. This will involve him indicating formally what he requires from a unit or system. The design specification will indicate how such requirements are to be achieved.

For day-to-day items, such as 'white goods', calculators and digital watches, the prospective customer does not get a chance to indicate his requirements, other than during a market research operation. On the other hand, today's customer has a wide range of competing goods from which to select. If one company will not give him what he wants, another will.

A *customer's* specification may be all well and good, but only a full *design* feasibility study will identify the cost. It may be that the specification cannot be met, even with 'state of the art' technology, or that the cost would be prohibitive. The *reliability* specification may demand *zero defects* - or as near as *possible*. *Aero space* industry units are extremely expensive due to these criteria.

# Introduction to Quality

A purely functional specification may not meet the customer's wishes, e.g, what happens if there is a power failure with a washing machine? Can the customer remove his laundry from the machine without a flood? The design specification must, therefore, see that a drainage point is fitted for this eventuality. In other words, specifications may include what must not happen as well as what must happen.

ISO 8402 lists twelve types of specification. It may be worth mentioning that one of these is a specification for disposal! If there is a policy to be *green* and *safe*, this will certainly refer to the disposal of, for example, refrigerators. An installation specification will ensure that no damage is done to the product during installation, which will affect its function. Installation specifications will also involve transport and packaging.

The designers and manufacturers of products are professional, whereas users may be non-technical or uneducated. This must be appreciated when writing user specifications.

# Standards and Specifications

## Material Specifications

### Introduction

To use materials for various purposes, the product designer and production engineer need detailed information to make the best choice from the viewpoint of a service and manufacturing requirement. The information is usually given as an engineering specification compiled by industry and organisations such as the British Standards Institution.

### Types of Specification:

The type of specification is important. For example, the designer is not really interested in the content of materials or their chemical make up but only in their performance during service.

Examples of specifications may include:

*Design Specification:* That might include a description of the primary purpose of an item, its style, function, performance, capacity, appearance, conditions of use, health and safety considerations, reliability, maintenance, materials, size, shape, colour, weight and tolerances allocated.

*Service Specification:* This defines the services to be carried out, the level of performance required (including response times), roles and responsibilities, rules for escalating problems which cannot be resolved locally, and so on.

*Test Specification*: A document that describes in detail the objectives and method of conducting tests, including the data, the test environment, equipment, data, conditions, criteria for assessing results.

*Customer Specification:* What the customer requires from the product that may include a large amount from the design specification information above.

Whatever the definition of the particular type of specification, there will be much overlap between them.

### Body of the Specification

Specifications may be written in a wide range of subjects and with a variety of objectives. The content of a specification depends upon the objectives to be achieved.

They may include 'product reliability specifications', 'colour specification', 'weight specification', 'safety specification', etc.

The production engineer is interested in that part of the specification that affects how materials are formed during the manufacturing process. The production and quality engineers are both interested in that part of the specification that affects the manufacturing process, which in turn affects the service specification. To this end, the content of a material and its microstructures under various manufacturing conditions may be very relevant. Examples of this may include 'weld decay' problems with stainless steels, the various treatments encountered during the processing of aluminium alloys, the heat treatment effects of carbon steels, melting temperatures, cast-ability and join-ability etc.

Research and Development personnel together with test engineers and metallurgists, will be interested in all aspects including detailed metallurgical analysis.

Many properties may be specified in numerical terms, e.g. strength in $Mn/m^2$. Others such as Malleability, may only be listed in order of the materials concerned.

**Specification Writing**

BS 7373 : 1991 Guide to the Preparation of Specifications provides rules for effective specification writing.

*A few simple rules*

Statements should be clear and concise not vague or ambiguous. In a specification for making tea, for example, it would be insufficient to state that the water must be clean. It would be necessary to specify the standard against which the quality of the water could be measured.

The purpose of a specification is to convey information. The ease with which this is achieved will be influenced by the style of presentation of this information. The standard provides guidance on this important aspect of specification preparation.

A specification should always include a statement of its objectives. The objectives of a specification may be to give guidance, to list requirements, to educate, to inform or to instruct. Generally, one or more of these would be described in the introduction.

# Standards and Specifications

Clarity of text is essential. Double or hidden meanings should be eliminated. Technical terms should be referenced or defined. The final text should be suitable for inclusion in a legally binding contract.

## *Terminology*

Specifications are written to be used by a variety of people. The technical level of the content may dictate the style to be adopted but, in the interests of clarity, the group, professional or non-professional, for whom the document is to be written, should be a major consideration.

The terminology used in the writing of a specification should be consistent with the specialist requirements of the subject and the comprehension of the user.

A specification written for use by members of a discrete profession would be expected to contain the terminology associated with the profession. A similar specification written for use by the consumer or user of a product or service should avoid highly technical terminology and, where appropriate, should use a graphical approach.

Consistent terminology should be used throughout the specification and the use of synonyms should be avoided. If a specification is part of a series, consistency with other specifications/standards should be ensured.

Terms or units used that could be misinterpreted or that are highly technical and pertinent to the subject matter of the specification should be defined.

Terms used in a special way for a particular specification should be defined.

Acronyms, no matter how well known to the author, should rarely be used and, if needed, should be preceded in the text by full terms the first time that they occur.

# Introduction to Quality

In summary, the prime requirements of a specification are for mutual understanding, clarity and simplicity, using plain and simple language. Consequently, the *specification* should be:

- As short as possible - unnecessary words or descriptions lead to lack of precision
- Positive in meaning and intent
- Unambiguous
- Specific and precise
- Free from vague generalities such as 'to be of good finish' or 'to be free from blemishes'. No questions such as 'how good?' or 'how free?' should remain unanswered
- Numerical wherever possible, e.g. surface finish should be specified by the CLA (centre line average) value
- Clear regarding the minimum acceptable level of quality or performance. Note: this may be affected by specifying the average and the range of characteristic required, such as a nominal dimension and the tolerance. For non-dimensional attributes, e.g. porosity, magnetic particle inspection indications of non-metallic inclusions, etc., the minimum acceptable level will be defined by the maximum size and number of blow-holes, and so on, in specified areas
- Augmented by photographs, diagrams, models or samples where a precise numerical value cannot be given
- Free from the common fallacy of calling for an unattainable 'desirable' target
- Supported, whenever possible, by national or company standards but only after it has been confirmed that the standards themselves are clearly expressed and precise in their meaning
- It is recommended that the convention for use of the words '*should*', '*shall*', '*must*' and '*will*' will be as follows:
  - '*should*' for guidance clauses where there are no requirement or compliance inferred
  - '*shall*' or '*must*' when a requirement to comply with the contents of the clause is mandatory.

## *Suggested order of specification presentation*

The suggested order of specification presentation is as follows:

- Identification:      title, designation, number, authority
- Issue number:      publication history and state of issue, earlier related specifications
- Contents list:      structure of the specification
- Foreword:      the reason for writing the specification

# Standards and Specifications

- Introduction: describes content in general and the technical aspects of objectives
- Scope: statement of what the specification applies to
- Definitions: terms used with meanings peculiar to the text
- Requirement/ guidance/ methods/elements    the main body of specification
- Appendices: examples, etc.
- Index: cross references
- References: to national, European, international standards or other internal company specifications.

## *Product specifications as a basis for contract and auditing*

Many large organisations, such as Marks & Spencer, rely totally on their suppliers delivering quality products and yet manage to maintain a very high reputation. This is achieved by requiring suppliers to comply strictly with product specifications. Typically, the specification for a shirt may be 50 to 100 pages long, detailing every element of manufacture. It would cover such things as cotton specification, including any starching or treatment to be applied to the textile, the gauge of the cotton, the length and positioning of stitching and so on. Marks & Spencer would then make regular surveillance visits to the supplier to audit that their specifications are being followed to the letter.

## *Specification amendments*

From time to time, modifying the quality standard will be necessary. Thus, changes may be requested by the customer, or the designer may wish to improve or correct his design. Either way, it is usually the designer who will arrange for the drawings and specifications to be altered. Strict control will then be necessary to make sure that everyone concerned  receives a revised copy, when they need it. The routine might be as follows:
- Copies of drawings and specifications are kept only in most suitably placed locations, usually drawing stores
- When any drawing is issued or re-issued, the prescribed number of copies is sent to each.  A person who requires a copy, borrows it from the nearest store, and his name is recorded
- Where a re-issue is concerned, all copies of the previous issue are recalled and destroyed.  Letting those in possession of the old issue destroy it is not satisfactory, because they will not always do so and then some time in the

future, an obsolete issue will appear. Work will be made to it before the mistake is discovered

o   Showing clearly the alterations made to it and the date is usual for the modified drawing
o   Sometimes a modified drawing contains an indication of the urgency of the changes, e.g.

a)   *Type 1 modification*    Very urgent. All partially completed work to the old drawings is to be scrapped and no more produced until the modified drawing can be used.

b)   *Type 2 modification*    Partially completed work that is to the old drawing can be completed, but no more is to be made to it.

c)   *Type 3 modification*    Changes to new issue as soon as convenient and economic. For example, when the tooling has to be renewed, or the present stocks of raw material run out.

The factory may wish to request a modification to the quality standard, to make the product easier and cheaper to produce. If the change is to be permanent, arrangements should be made with the designer to have the drawing altered and re-issued. Sometimes the request is more temporary. Perhaps the material specified cannot be obtained in time, or the factory wish to use up similar material already in stock. In such cases, the factory will request a *production permit*, authorising them to produce to the modified standard. Such permits are issued before production, and are only valid for a limited period. Permanent changes should be covered by a modification to the drawing.

## Concession procedures

From time to time a batch may be produced outside drawing limits, which, although the inspectors will rightly reject, nevertheless could be used. The factory will then ask for a *concession*. This allows them to use the product that has already been made, but they are not permitted to produce any more like it. The term *deviation* or *quality deviation* is sometimes used to embrace both production permits and concessions.

When any changes in the quality standard are authorised, care must be taken to deal with any repercussions, thus consequential changes may be necessary to certain components, otherwise the final performance and reliability of the product may be affected. Consequently, concessions are usually considered by a team of interested parties before it is agreed. It is important that long term preventive action is considered, e.g. re-design.

For the relationship between specifications measurement and process capability see the Section "Relationship between Specifications Measurement and Process Capability" on page 181.

# Introduction to Quality

## Principles of Measurement

Before the advent of the Industrial Revolution with all its ramifications, measurements were achieved by many varied and peculiar methods such as, length by various parts of the anatomy; time, by using sun dials, hour glasses and burning candles; mass by using various lumps of metal.

Although there were many precursors to standardisation during the nineteenth century, many items were made in their entirety by one person with no need for interchangeability. Since the craftsman saw the whole job through from start to finish every part was made to fit all the other parts with little thought for standardisation. It was not until Henry Ford's re-engineering of the motor car that the concept became universal "you can have any colour as long as it's black".

Today's industry, with its mass producing, interchangeable systems, needs highly accurate length measurement. In the pharmaceutical industry mass needs to be measured in milligrams or less. The industry which has grown up around Einstein's theories, require timing devices accurate to a $10^{-12}$ seconds (picos).

### *Parameters and metrics*

b) A parameter is a variable which can be measured, such as temperature, time, length, time to repair, shutter speed etc.
c) A metric is the value of a parameter, e.g. 150 mm, 5 seconds, 100° C.

### *Accuracy and precision*

d) Accuracy is how close a measurement is to the specified metric.
e) Precision is the repeatability of such a measurement.

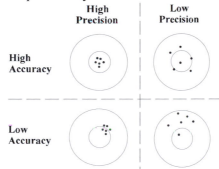

**Figure 7** Accuracy and Precision

# Natural, Material and Subjective Standards

## Basic Standards of Measurements

Modern technology requires, where possible, absolute, unvarying, primary standards of measurement.

## Natural, Material and Subjective Standards

The following is an extract from a letter written by the late C.R. Shotbolt - one time IQA Chief Examiner. The letter describes Mr C.R. Shotbolt's interpretation of the definition of various terms used in Measurements, Standards and Specifications.

---

*Natural, material and subjective standards explained*

*Natural standards*

*Some units of measurements are referred to standards which are themselves natural phenomena. The metre is referred to the distance light travels in a vacuum in a specified time. Time is itself referred to a natural standard: the frequency of oscillation of the radiation emitted by isotope 133 of the atom of caesium. Temperature is also referred to a natural standard: the freezing point of water. These are all expressed here in a simplified form, the actual definition being much more complex. (Until recently the standard of length was the wavelength of the orange/red radiation in the spectrum of isotope 86 of the gas krypton. As length is still measured using interferometry involving the wavelength of light, either velocity or wavelength would be acceptable as an answer to this examiner's questions regarding the natural standard of length.) Any standards officer could set up a natural standard if he was prepared to buy the right equipment, and, for instance, calibrate reference gauges for length directly against the wavelength of light.*

*Material standards*

*The unit of mass, the kilogram, is referred to the International Kilogram which is a mass of an alloy of platinum and iridium kept at the International Bureau of Standards at Sevres in France. It is a man-made object and has a mass of precisely one kg because international agreement was reached which said so. It cannot be precisely copied and if damaged or destroyed it cannot be exactly replaced.*

*If a trading standards officer wished to have his standard masses checked, they would have to be calibrated against reference masses held for the purpose at a suitable laboratory. These would have to be checked regularly against a copy of the British version of the international kg held at NPL. The British copy is checked regularly against the international kg in France. At each of these comparisons there might be an error as no measurement is exact, and, cumulatively, the greater the number of levels of comparison between the shop scales and the*

---

*international kg the greater must be the allowance for error in the calibration of the scales. This is what is meant when reference is made to a hierarchy of measurements.*

*Subjective Standards*

*There are cases when a decision as to whether or not an item should be accepted or rejected cannot depend upon an objective measurement but has to rely on a subjective judgement. Taste, smell, flaws in glass components or a paint finish are all examples. In many cases it is possible to have an example to which the inspector can refer and with which the item under test can be compared. Such an example is a subjective standard.*

*It has been suggested that, as the words 'natural standard', 'material standard' and 'subjective standard' do not appear in literature published by the British Standards Institution, they should not be used in an IQA syllabus. Although I had nothing to do with writing the syllabus, I cannot agree with this view. The words express exactly the differences between the different types of standards. Whereas BSI may be concerned with writing a specification on the measurement of length and another on the type of scales to be used for determining the mass of a particular item, I cannot see them having a need to distinguish between natural and material standards in order to explain the advantages of one over the other.*

*Incidentally, should we not get back to referring to British Standard Specifications rather than British Standards. It takes longer to say but it could avoid some confusion.*

All measurements can be derived from the six fundamental units of the SI (Systems International) systems which are:
o   mass
o   length
o   temperature
o   electric current
o   luminous intensity
o   time.

# Natural, Material and Subjective Standards

## The International System of Units[2] (SI)

Formal definitions of all SI base units are approved by the Conférence Générale des Poids et Mesures (CGPM). The first such definition was approved in 1889 and the most recent in 1983. These definitions are modified from time to time as techniques of measurement evolve and allow more accurate realisations of the base units. The Bureau International des Poids et Mesures (BIPM) operates under the exclusive supervision of the Comité International des Poids et Mesures (CIPM) which itself comes under the authority of the CGPM and reports to it on the work accomplished by the BIPM. The BIPM was set up by the Convention du Mètre signed in Paris on 20 May 1875 by seventeen states during the final session of the diplomatic Conference of the Metre. This convention was amended in 1921[3]. The BIPM has its headquarters near Paris. The task of the BIPM is to ensure world-wide unification of physical measurements; its function is thus to:
o    establish fundamental standards and scales for the measurement of the principal physical quantities and maintain the international prototypes
o    carry out comparisons of national and international standards
o    ensure the coordination of corresponding measuring techniques
o    carry out and coordinate measurements of the fundamental physical constants relevant to these activities.

SI units are divided into two classes:
o    *base* units
o    *derived* units.

The International System is based on a choice of seven well-defined units which by convention are regarded as dimensionally independent:
1.  the metre
2.  the kilogram
3.  the second
4.  the ampere
5.  the kelvin
6.  the mole

---

[2]    The following section is based on text and diagrams which are © Crown Copyright 2000 and reproduced by permission of the Controller of HMSO

[3]    As of 31 December 1997, forty-eight States were members of this Convention

7.  the candela.

These SI units are called *base units*.

The second class of SI units is that of *derived units*. These are units that are formed as products of powers of the base units according to the algebraic relations linking the quantities concerned.

Examples of SI derived units expressed in terms of base units

| Quantity | SI unit | |
|---|---|---|
| | **Name** | **Symbol** |
| area | square metre | $m^2$ |
| volume | cubic metre | $m^3$ |
| speed, velocity | metre per second | m/s |
| acceleration | metre per second squared | $m/s^2$ |
| wave number | 1 per metre | $m^{-1}$ |
| density, mass density | kilogram per cubic metre | $kg/m^3$ |
| specific volume | cubic metre per kilogram | $m^3/kg$ |
| current density | ampere per square metre | $A/m^2$ |
| magnetic field strength | ampere per metre | A/m |
| luminance | candela per square metre | $cd/m^2$ |

Other SI units having their own names:

| | | | |
|---|---|---|---|
| frequency | hertz | Hz | $s^{-1}$ |
| force | newton | N | $m\ kg\ s^{-2}$ |
| pressure, stress | pascal | Pa | $m^{-1}\ kg\ s^{-2}$ |
| energy, work quantity of heat | joule | J | $m^2\ kg\ s^{-2}$ |
| power, radiant flux | watt | W | $J/s\ m^2\ kg\ s^{-3}$ |
| electric charge, quantity of electricity | coulomb | C | $s\ A$ |
| electric potential, potential difference, electromotive force | volt | V | $m^2\ kg\ s^{-3}\ A^{-1}$ |
| capacitance | farad | F | $m^{-2}\ kg^{-1}\ s^4\ A^2$ |
| electric resistance | ohm | $\Omega$ | $m^2\ kg\ s^{-3}\ A^{-2}$ |
| electric conductance | siemens | S | $m^{-2}\ kg^{-1}\ s^3\ A^2$ |
| magnetic flux | weber | Wb | $m^2\ kg\ s^{-2}\ A^{-1}$ |
| magnetic flux density | tesla | T | $kg\ s^{-2}\ A^{-1}$ |
| inductance | henry | H | $m^2\ kg\ s^{-2}\ A^{-2}$ |
| luminous flux | lumen | lm | $cd\ m^2\ m^{-2} = cd$ |
| illuminance | lux | lx | $cd\ m^2\ m^{-4} = cd\ m^{-2}$ |

# Natural, Material and Subjective Standards

## *Mass[4] - kilogram (kg)*

Mass is a material standard. Although other units of measure may have secondary material standards for convenience, mass is the only remaining standard which is not based on some natural phenomena. The mass of a body is defined as the quantity of matter of which the body consists and can only be changed if matter is added to or subtracted from the body.

**Definition:** *The kilogram is the unit of mass; it is equal to the mass of the international prototype of the kilogram.*

The fundamental unit of mass is the international prototype of the kilogram made of an alloy of platinum (90%) and iridium (10%) and is kept at the International Bureau of Weights and Measures (BIMP) at Sevres, France. Duplicates are held by various countries including Great Britain (in the custody of the National Physical Laboratory (NPL)) and may be compared with the prototype on request. Comparisons can be made with accurate scales to 1 in $10^8$ precision.

The main problem with a physical object is that its mass could change due to the loss of material or contamination from the surrounding environment. The mass of the international prototype could be slightly greater or less today than it was when it was made in 1884 but there is no way of proving this. Another problem is the effort it takes to maintain a traceable chain between, for example, your bathroom scales and the kilogram. The prototype has not emerged from its box since 1941 and, in practise, transfer standards are compared with the average of seven duplicate standard masses.

Research is going on in a number of scientific laboratories to try to find a way of defining the kilogram in terms of a fundamental constant.

---

[4] In everyday situations the weight of an object is the same as its mass. However, if the same object were taken into space, the mass would stay the same but the object would become weightless.

*Length - metre (m)*

**Definition:** *The metre is the length of the path travelled by light in vacuum during a time interval of 1/299,792,458th of a second.*

Historically, as with mass, length standards were based upon physical standards, i.e. the distance between two lines or the distance between two parallel ends of a bar.

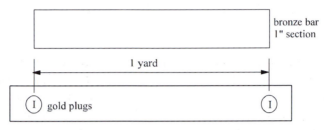

**Figure 8** Imperial Standard Yard

Such standards are prone to secular change, i.e. changes in dimension, over a period due to their metallurgical structure. Also, difficulty was experienced in transferring the accuracy to secondary and tertiary standards. The 1889 definition of the metre, based on the international prototype, was replaced in 1960 using a definition based upon a wavelength of krypton 86 radiation.

Today, in practise, length is measured using interferometry which uses a standard light source to create interference patterns similar to the rainbow colours found in oil films on water. As the edge of the oil tapers away, colour fringes are formed by the light. The distance between two adjacent bands of the same colour are equal to the wavelength of the light source and is the change in thickness of the oil film.

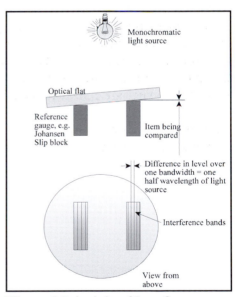

**Figure 9** Principle of Interferometry

# Natural, Material and Subjective Standards

## Temperature - kelvin (K[5])

The two most common measures of temperature in everyday use named after Gabriel Daniel Fahrenheit and Professor Anders Celsius respectively. A third, fundamental temperature scale widely used by physicists and engineers is the kelvin, symbol K, named after the Scottish physicist Lord Kelvin. The unit of Celsius temperature is the degree Celsius, symbol °C, which is by definition equal in magnitude to the kelvin, but has its base point zero corresponding to the melting point of ice or 273.16 K.

*Definition: The kelvin, unit of thermodynamic temperature, is the fraction 1/273.16 of the thermodynamic temperature of the triple point of water.*

This temperature starts at absolute zero. The coldest that anything can exist. At this temperature, all molecular movement comes to a halt and materials start to display unusual properties such as super-conductivity as they approach this temperature.

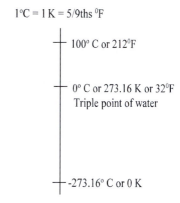

*Triple point of water:* At low pressure, water may co-exist in its three forms, i.e. solid, liquid and gas at the same temperature. This is referred to as the triple point of water, which for all intents and purposes is the temperature at which ice melts.

**Figure 10**
Temperature scales in common use

## Practical temperature measurement

*Thermometers* - liquid-in-glass, particularly mercury, thermometers rely on the expansion of a fluid with temperature. The fluid is contained in a sealed glass tube and the temperature is read using a scale etched along the stem of the thermometer.

*Platinum resistance* - electrical thermometers which make use of the variation in resistance of high-purity platinum wire with temperature. They are very sensitive and, with sophisticated equipment, measurements can routinely be better than a thousandth part of 1 °C.

---

[5] Units named after a person always start with a capital letter

# Introduction to Quality

*Thermocouples* - are the most common sensors in industrial use. They consist of two dissimilar metallic conductors joined at the point of measurement. When the conductors are heated, a voltage is generated in the circuit and this can be used to determine the temperature.

*Radiation (or pyrometers)* - make use of the fact that all objects emit thermal radiation as seen when looking at the bars of an electric fire or light bulb. The amount of radiation emitted can be measured and related to temperature using the Planck law of radiation. Temperatures can be measured remotely using this technique, with the sensor situated some distance away from the object. Hence it is useful to use this for objects that are very hot, moving or in hazardous environments.

## Realisation and use at the National Physical Laboratory

Triple point of water cells are used at NPL to realise the triple-point temperature (273.16 K) with a reproducibility of 0.1 mK. Other temperatures may be related to this via the International Temperature Scale in terms of which platinum resistance and other thermometers are calibrated within the range of 0.65 K to 3000 K.

## Practical references for calibrating temperature scales

By using the melting points of various substances (°C)

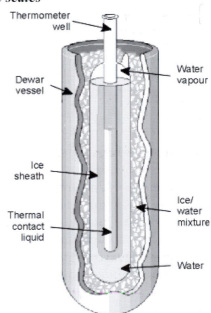

e.g.

| | |
|---|---|
| liquid and gaseous oxygen | 182.97 |
| ice and water | 0.0 |
| water and vapour | 100.0 |
| liquid sulphur and vapour | 444.6 |
| solid silver and liquid silver | 960.5 |
| solid gold and liquid gold | 1063.0 |
| mercury | -38.8 |
| lead | 327.0 |
| zinc | 419.4 |
| copper | 1083.0 |
| tungsten | 3400.0 |

**Figure 11** Triple Point of Water Cell

*Electric current - ampere (A)*

**Definition:** *The ampere is that constant current which, if maintained in two straight parallel conductors of infinite length of negligible circular cross-section, and placed 1metre apart in vacuum, would produce between those conductors a force equal to 2 x 10 $^{-7}$ newton per metre of length.*

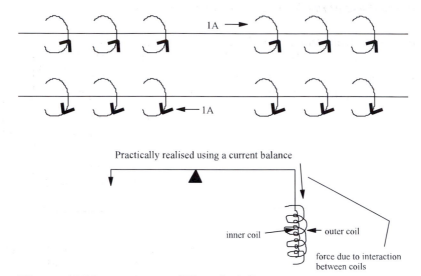

**Figure 12** Measurement of Electrical Current

*Realisation and use at the National Physical Laboratory*

The ampere is realised, via the watt, to about 0.08 μA using NPL's current-weighing and induced-emf method. The ohm is realised at NPL via a Thompson-Lampard calculable capacitor to about 0.05 μΩ and maintained via the quantised Hall resistance to about 0.01 μΩ. The volt is maintained to 0.01 μV using the Josephson effects of superconductivity.

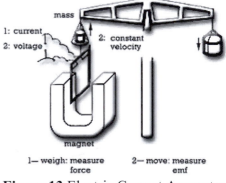

**Figure 13** Electric Current Apparatus

# Introduction to Quality

## *Luminous intensity - candela (cd)*

***Definition:*** *The candela is the luminous intensity, in a given direction, of a source that emits monochromatic radiation of frequency 540 x 10¹² hertz and that has a radiant intensity in that direction of (1/683) watts per steradian (see below).*

## *Realisation and use at the National Physical Laboratory*

The candela has been realised at NPL with an uncertainty of 0.2%, using a cryogenic radiometer which equates the heating effect of optical radiation with that of electric power.

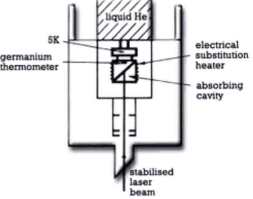

**Figure 14** Luminous Intensity Apparatus

In practise a series of filament lamps is used to calibrate light sources.

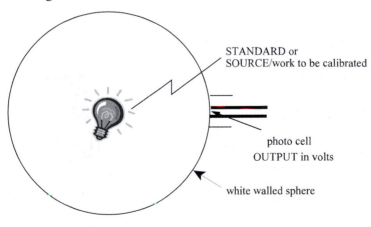

**Figure 15** Comparison of Light Source with Standard

# Natural, Material and Subjective Standards

## Time - second (s)

**Definition:** *The second is the duration of 9,192,631,770 periods of the radiation corresponding to the transition between the two hyperfine levels of the ground state of the caesium 133 atom.*

Fundamentally, all man-made clocks are set by some naturally occurring clock, e.g. the cycle time of a swinging pendulum or the 24 hour rotation of the earth which used to be the standard of time. The complete rotation of the earth was timed by recording the instant a point on the earth passed under a chosen star in the sky on successive nights. The interval was divided into 24 x 60 x 60 = 86,400 parts which was defined as one second. However, there are errors due to the wobble in the earth's rotation on its axis. The rate of rotation of the earth itself fluctuates unpredictably, hence, an error of one part in 20 million is apparent. This may seem incredibly accurate but it is not good enough for present day technology.

Caesium is a silvery metal liquid at room temperature. Other substances such as ammonia have been used to regulate atomic clocks but caesium is the most accurate to 1 part in $10^{13}$, i.e. 1sec in 300,000 years.

## Realisation and use at the National Physical Laboratory

The second is realised by primary caesium frequency standards to about 2 parts in $10^{15}$ - equivalent to a second in 15 million years. The majority are traditional caesium-beam designs *(see diagram),* but the latest use lasers to control and detect the atoms. They calibrate Co-ordinated Universal Time (UTC) which is broadcast globally by radio and navigation satellites.

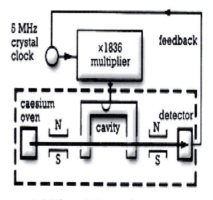

**Figure 16** Time Measuring Apparatus

# Introduction to Quality

## Amount of Substance - mole (mol)

Following the discovery of the fundamental laws of chemistry, units called, for example, "gram - atom" and "gram - molecule", were used to specify amounts of chemical elements or compounds. These units had a direct connection with "atomic weights" and "molecular weights", which are in fact relative masses.

It remained to define the unit of amount of substance by fixing the corresponding mass of carbon 12; by international agreement this mass was fixed at 0.012 kg, and the unit of the quantity "amount of substance" was given the name *mole* (symbol mol).

***Definition:*** *The mole is the amount of substance of a system which contains as many elementary entities as there are atoms in 0.012 kilogram of carbon 12; its symbol is "mol".*

Note: When the mole is used, the elementary entities must be specified and may be atoms, molecules, ions, electrons, other particles, or specified groups of such particles.

In this definition, it is understood that unbound atoms of carbon 12, at rest and in their ground state, are referred to.

## Angular Measurement

In addition to the seven fundamental units of measurement, angles are defined as follows:

### *Plane angle - radian (rad)*

**Definition:** *The radian is the plane angle between two radii of a circle which cut off on the circumference an arc equal in length to the radius.*

1 radian is $360/\pi$ or approximately 57 degrees.

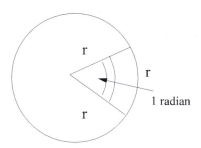

**Figure 17** Radian

### *Solid angle - Steradian (Sr)*

Definition: The steradian is the solid angle which, having its vertex in the centre of a sphere, cuts off an area of the surface of the sphere equal to that of a square with sides of length equal to the radius of the sphere.

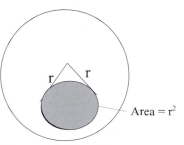

**Figure 18** Steradian

### *Realisation and use at the National Physical Laboratory*

These quantities are to be regarded as dimensionless derived units[6] which may be used or omitted in the expression for derived units. NPL angle calibrations achieve an accuracy of < 0.1 arc second. This would correspond to a navigation error of about two metres in crossing the Atlantic from New York to London.

---

[6]     Now derived units, their separate designation as supplementary units was abrogated by the CIPM 1995. International Committee for Weights and Measures (CIPM, *Comité International des Poids et Mesures*)

## Calibration Concepts Techniques and Systems

Calibration is defined in ISO 8402/BS4778 and BS5233 as "All the operations for determining the values of the errors of measuring equipment (and, if necessary, to determine other metrological properties)".

The importance of regular calibration of gauges and measuring equipment cannot be over-emphasised. An organisation's effectiveness and the quality and reliability of its products rely upon an efficient calibration system. Without such a system operating precision would be unknown.

Calibration is the checking of an instrument, article, or device against a known standard, usually of a much lower order than the primary standard.

Calibration is expensive, and the cost increases rapidly with reduced uncertainty, but the cost of being 'out of calibration' can be out of all proportion to the calibration cost. As an indication, to halve the uncertainty increases costs tenfold. Health and safety aspects may also have to be taken into account apart from cost.

### Frequency of calibration

The frequency of calibration depends upon a number of factors:

- stability, sensitivity to change
- usage, frequency, handling
- environment,
- precision required.

### Identification and status marking

Inspection, measuring and test equipment should be suitably identified together with its calibration status. This usually takes the form of a label with a serial number and a 'Calibration due' date so that the user can determine that it is safe to use.

Equipment not intended to determine the final quality of a product may not need to be calibrated. In such cases the equipment should be marked 'Un-calibrated'. Other suitable labelling may be appropriate in certain circumstances, for example, 'calibrate before use'.

# Calibration Concepts Techniques and Systems

## *Uncertainty*

Just as tolerances are applied to work for economic reasons, the same is used for gauges and instruments. The tolerance of a gauge is referred to as the uncertainty of measurement since there cannot be any confidence of anything less than that when using that particular gauge. When calibration procedures are prepared, they should define the uncertainty within which they are to be calibrated. In general, the gauge or instrument precision should be ten times better than the item it is used to measure. However, four or five times is often adequate. The fact remains that the precision to which we measure is limited by the next level of measurement.

## *Traceability*

Calibration may be carried out in-house provided that the standard used for calibration is itself calibrated to traceable standards. All technological quantities have standards which are traceable to reliable primary standards.

Assuming that each subsequent checking media is ten times as accurate as the previous one the following table shows the traceable steps of calibration from the work to national primary standards.

| CALIBRATION DEVICE | UNCERTAINTY mm | TYPE OF STD | ORGANISATION |
|---|---|---|---|
| **WORK** | 0.01 | ---------------- | |
| measured by | ↓ | ↓ | |
| **MICROMETER** | 0.001 | Workshop | Workshop |
| calibrated by | ↓ | ↓ | ↓ |
| **SLIP GAUGE** | 0.0001 | Tertiary | Inspection room |
| calibrated by | ↓ | ↓ | ↓ |
| **OPTICAL FLAT** | 0.00001 | Secondary | Standards laboratory |
| Calibrated by | ↓ | ↓ | ↓ |
| **LIGHT** | 0.000001 | Primary | NAMAS[7] accredited laboratory |

---

[7]    In a later section the role of the National Assessment and Measurement Accreditation Scheme (NAMAS) is explained in more depth.

# Introduction to Quality

There may, of course, be other checks within the calibration procedures of any feature which may impair the use of the equipment, e.g. flatness and parallelism of micrometer anvils.

The above chart will obviously vary from industry to industry, and from physical quantity to physical quantity, but the principle remains the same. It is obviously impossible to go from a workshop situation, directly to the primary standard. The direct traceable link from the lowest possible situation, e.g. length in a workshop, mass in the grocer's shop, ordinary everyday time keeping, to the primary standard, in each case, must be via a well-organised system.

## Calibration Systems

The following list describes the key requirements of a calibration system as required in ISO 9001.

i. Identify all measuring equipment with a unique identification, e.g. serial number and its calibration status. See Table - Calibration Labelling.

**Table 2** Calibration Labelling

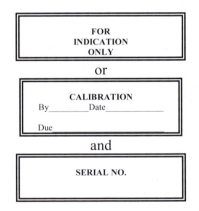

ii. Establish the frequency with which the measuring equipment needs to be checked, e.g. for a set of weighing scales this could be every six months.

iii. Define procedures that describe the calibration system (measuring equipment recall procedure etc.). This can be a card file; one card for each piece of measuring equipment. The cards are then filed in next-calibration-date order, so at the beginning of each month the equipment that requires calibration is identified and located.

**Table 3** A Typical Calibration History Sheet

| CALIBRATION HISTORY RECORD SHEET | | | | | |
|---|---|---|---|---|---|
| Equipment Type: | | | Model No.: | | |
| Serial No.: | | | Size: | | |
| Calibration Frequency: | | | Procedure No.: | | |
| DATE OF LAST CALIBRATION | DATE OF NEXT CALIBRATION | DATE OUT/IN | LOCATION | RESULT OF CALIBRATION | REMARKS |
| | | | | | |

iv.    Detail the individual calibration procedures for each type of measuring equipment. For weighing scales this could be having some calibrated weights placed on the scales and checking the readings correspond with the calibrated weights.

v.    Ensure that the inspection and test equipment has the necessary accuracy and precision. For the weighing scales example the accuracy of the calibrated weights could be 10% of the accuracy of the scales.

vi.    Define the procedures that describe the activities necessary if the results of calibration highlight equipment error. If the weighing scales were found to be in error when calibrated and used for weighing drugs, then it may be necessary to take corrective action, possibly to recall the drugs.

vii.    Establish calibration history records showing the previous calibration results. **Table 3** shows a typical calibration history sheet.

viii.    Determine the necessary environmental conditions suitable for accurate calibration.

ix.    Detail appropriate handling, preservation and storage procedures.

x.  Ensure that equipment is sealed to avoid any possibility of adjustments that could invalidate the calibration setting. For the weighing scales - any adjustment screws would need to be sealed.

**Calibration and Automatic Test Equipment (ATE)**

ATE equipment is computer controlled test equipment, frequently used for the testing of assemblies and sub-assemblies. Typically these types of machines have either an 'in circuit' or a 'functional' test capability (or a combination of both).

'In circuit' testing confirms that a circuit board has been manufactured correctly (i.e. finds short circuits, open circuits and components that are outside tolerance limits). The in circuit tester usually interfaces with the unit under test (UUT) via a 'bed of nails' fixture that has one pin for every electrical node. This allows measurement of characteristics between any electrical connections (e.g. across each component). **Figure 19** shows a typical ATE set up. 'Functional' testing interfaces to the UUT either via a few pins in a bed of nails fixture (e.g. maybe one pin per 100 connections) or by way of flying leads. This means of testing could be used for a printed circuit board or a whole assembly. A 'good' functional test will find any manufacturing defects plus any parameters that are not within design specifications.

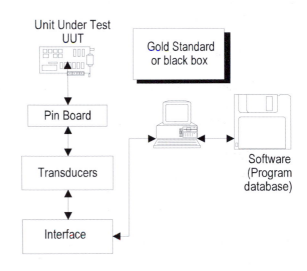

**Figure 19** Typical Automatic Test Equipment

Functional testing is quick to highlight a failure whereas in circuit testing is quicker to pinpoint where the failure lies, (i.e. identifies the fault location down to component level). A typical use for ATE is in medium to high volume production or for high level technology, such as the space industry.

# Calibration Concepts Techniques and Systems

The use of automatic testing ensures that all the assemblies are tested to within pre-defined tolerances. The testing becomes objective as opposed to subjective. The QA personnel would need to ensure that the pre-selected tolerances are correct. Once proven this method of testing provides a very high degree of repeatability plus the availability of automatically logged test results for use in Statistical Quality Control (SQC) and real time fault analysis (RTFA).

Calibration of the equipment, i.e. transducers and connection between the equipment under test and the computer; the transducer and connection between the computer and the pin board can be tested, although not completely, by the use of a 'Gold Standard' or 'Black Box'. This 'Gold Standard' could be a specially selected unit that is a known standard or quality. This 'Gold Standard' would be regularly re-tested by the ATE to confirm that the hardware is working satisfactorily.

Validation and verification of the test software program and data for ATE could consist of:

i.      the program to drive the ATE
ii.     the sequencer which runs the sequence and determines which test to perform
iii.    the test data (both target value and tolerance), the program and sequencer will need to be validated and verified. The test data will need to be checked.

## Specifications, Measurements and Process Capability

Since measurement is itself a process, it will have its own process capability. This is referred to as the uncertainty of measurement. The relationship between the process capability and the uncertainty of measurement may be appreciated by reference to Specifications Measurements and Process Capability Page 181.

In-process inspection means monitoring the process during production, by periodically inspecting samples and plotting the results on a chart. This is called Statistical Process Control or SPC for short. See page 182 for further details.

Inspection and Testing Methodology

## Introduction

### The Changing Role of Inspectors, Operators and Supervisors

Traditionally the purpose of inspection was to filter out defective work from being further processed or reaching the customer.  Work which can be salvaged is returned up the line for re-working.  With the new approach, the purpose of inspection is to collect information about the process as part of an information system and, instead of defective work being fed back, information is relayed to operators and setters so that the process controls can be adjusted to prevent future defectives being made.  In many circumstances, since inspection is being done 'on the job', periodically it is feasible and sensible that the inspection and recording of inspection results is done by the operator.

In earlier sections it was possible to see that the role of inspection has changed from that of detection to an element of control.  That is not to say that defects found are ignored.  Next to be considered, in more detail, is the role of inspection.

## Definition

Inspection is the process of measuring, examining, testing, gauging or otherwise comparing an item with the applicable requirements.

The inspection function is therefore concerned with:

1. Interpreting the specification or requirement
2. Measurement of the particular characteristic
3. Comparing (1) with (2)
4. Judging conformance
5. Disposing of conforming cases
6. Disposing of non-conforming cases
7. Recording the data obtained.

Inspection may be used for a number of purposes, each aimed at improving quality:

a. To distinguish acceptable items from unacceptable items
b. To distinguish acceptable lots from unacceptable lots
c. To determine if the process is changing
d. To rate the quality of a process (process average)

e. To rate the accuracy of inspectors or operators
f. To measure the precision of a measuring instrument
g. To measure the process capability.

## Inspection Techniques

There are three basic inspection techniques which can be used:
1. sorting or judgmental inspection
2. detection inspection - informative inspection
3. preventive inspection - source inspection.

1. Sorting Inspection - is a sorting process which segregates the defects from the acceptable items. This action prevents defects from being received by the customer but does not prevent further defects from being made. This is the traditional approach.

2. Detection Inspection - is an investigation of the causes of defective items with the objective of eventually taking corrective action to prevent recurrence.

3. Preventive Inspection - is inspection of the potential causes of defects preventing sources of defect occurring, avoiding the production of defects in the first place. Poka-yoke may be considered one method which could be employed to achieve this objective, i.e. automatically 100% inspecting or eliminating the potential causes of defects. There are three stages or elements to the Preventive Inspection approach:
   i. An understanding of the factors that can cause the defects.
   ii. Fail safe techniques which prevent the factor which cause defects.
   iii. Immediate action which stops the process in the event of a mistake being made, until the causes of the mistake are understood and fail safe mechanisms are established.

## *Inspection errors*

There are a number of potential inspection errors and Juran spoke of three: technique, inadvertent and willful errors. Nikkan Kogyo Shimbun speaks of ten: forgetfulness, misunderstanding, identification, amateurs, willful, inadvertent, slowness, lack of standard, surprise and intentional errors. Philip Crosby talks of two: lack of knowledge and lack of attention. All other errors are as a result of these two types. Confused? Well it may not matter too much as long as error causes are understood and an approach is adopted to prevent errors occurring.

# Inspection and Testing Methodology

## Types of errors

*Forgetful errors* - Absent-mindedness can happen for a number of reasons: lack of concentration, a moment's inattention could cause an error to occur. Possible prevention methods are: check lists, automatic safe guards, work reorganisation and using the Poka-Yoke approach.

*Misunderstanding* - It is easy to misconstrue instructions or commands if they are not clear (*"Into the valley of death rode the five hundred"*) and as a consequence, take the wrong action. Possible prevention methods are; written instructions, training, first off checks.

*Wrong Identification* - Wrong categorisation or designation of an item, file or quantity can result in expensive errors. Clear methods of identification need to be established: tagging or labelling, colour coding (although one in ten are colour blind to some degree), photographs, examples etc.

*Lack of Experience* - Lack of preparation for tasks and activities not only extends the start up time but also makes errors more likely. Possible prevention methods include: induction training, improved selection procedures, skill building, certification of inspectors, competent employees.

*Willful Errors* - Intentional errors can occur either due to deliberate mistakes or just because the rules were ignored. Possible prevention methods include: education, discipline.

## *Possible defect causes*

Listed are just some possible defect causes. These defect causes have been analysed with the different types of error to determine if there are any strong links.

Possible defect causes

| | | |
|---|---|---|
| Omitted operation | Faulty processing | Wrong location |
| Missing parts | Wrong part | Equipment adjustment fault |
| Incorrect set up | Faulty equipment | |

## Comparison of Error Types with Causes

| | Forgetful | Misunderstanding | Wrong Identification | Lack of Experience | Willful Error |
|---|---|---|---|---|---|
| Omitted Operation | ⊙ | O | O | O | ⊙ |
| Faulty Processing | ⊙ | ⊙ | O | ⊙ | ⊙ |
| Wrong Location | ⊙ | O | ⊙ | ⊙ | ⊙ |
| Missing Part | ⊙ | △ | ⊙ | △ | △ |
| Wrong Part | O | △ | △ | △ | △ |
| Equipment Adjustment Fault | △ | ⊙ | △ | ⊙ | △ |
| Incorrect Setup | △ | ⊙ | ⊙ | O | ⊙ |
| Faulty Equipment | ⊙ | △ | △ | △ | △ |

⊙ Strong Link

O Medium Link

△ Weak Link

# Inspection and Testing Methodology

## Inspection Planning

As products and services have become more complex and as the job of providing them has been divided among many departments, the job of inspection has also become complex and divided. Most inspection is now done by inspectors who lack full understanding of fitness for use. For this more complex work, it has been found necessary to engage in formal inspection planning, i.e. preparing a written plan of what to inspect for and how.

### *Method*

1. The planner visits the various locations, interviews the key people, observes the activities, and records his findings in the form of a flow diagram.

2. Selection is then made of the inspection station, e.g.

   Receipt Inspection - at movement of goods and materials between companies, usually at Goods Inwards

   First-off inspection - before starting a costly or irreversible operation

   Process inspection - at movement of goods between departments of critical processes

   Final inspection - upon completion of the product.

3. Inspection instructions are prepared which tell the inspector:

   a. Which features to check

   b. How to decide whether an item conforms or not

   c. What to do with conforming and non-conforming items

   d. Who to inform about non-conformity

   e. What records to make.

4.     Inspection procedures are compiled.

The inspector needs to be told how to carry out the inspection and what instruments or gauges to use.


5.     Suitable documentation for inspection records is designed.

In addition to inspection planning for production, it may also be useful to consider inspection planning for such activities as:

| | | |
|---|---|---|
| Internal handling | - | use of correct containers and other handling facilities, product protection against corrosion and damage, etc. |
| Internal storage | - | adequate identity and traceability. |
| Packing | - | product identification, traceability, protection against environments, completeness, etc. |
| Shipping | - | care in loading, special markings, etc. |

## *How much inspection?*

The amount of inspection required at any stage is largely dependent on prior knowledge of previous experience.


1.     Prior knowledge of the process:

a.     In many cases the process is so inherently stable that a first-off and last-off check is sufficient, e.g. press operations.

b.     If the process capability is known it is sufficient to take samples at intervals known to be well within the time taken for the process to change, i.e. use of control charts.

c.     Operators or suppliers who have earned a reputation for high conformity obviously require less inspection than those who lack such records.

2.    Product fluidity/continuity.

Once it has been established that a fluid or continuous product is satisfactorily homogeneous, it is necessary only to take small samples which need not be random, e.g. a short length of steel from the end of a long bar.

3.    Non-critical features.

When deciding how much inspection the consequences of too little inspection must be considered. Obviously some features will not be critical and, therefore, not require regular inspection, e.g. non-functional dimensions.

Obtaining prior knowledge may require some effort on the part of the inspection planner. Such information may not always be readily available and may require special tests or experiments.

## *Decision making on fitness for use*

It is necessary to give careful consideration to the delegation of decision- making about the acceptance or otherwise of items.

Case 1    The item is realistically specified in an objective manner in such a way that the item can readily be classified as fit for use or not. Such decisions can be safely delegated to the inspector or even the operator.

Case 2    The item is realistically specified but in a subjective manner such as "surface must be scratch-free". Decisions of acceptance can only be delegated to the operator or inspector providing he has an adequate means of discriminating good from bad items, e.g. samples and training sessions.

Case 3    The item is not realistically toleranced and is the subject of discretion which varies with pressures such as urgency. It is unfair to subject inspectors to varying standards and it is usual to 'draw the line' and any non-conforming items will only be accepted as a result of the issue of a *'concession note'*. Such a concession note should only be issued after consultation by a committee at an appropriate level consistent with the consequences of the decision.

## *Control of non-conforming product*

Where non-conforming items or products have been found, procedures need to be established and implemented that identify and, if appropriate, segregate the non-conforming material or product until such time as a decision can be made as to the action necessary, e.g concessions, rework, scrap, regrade, etc.

Evaluation of suspect material: If suspect material is found, a possible approach that can be adopted in determining what action to take is detailed in **Figure 20**.

# Inspection and Testing Methodology

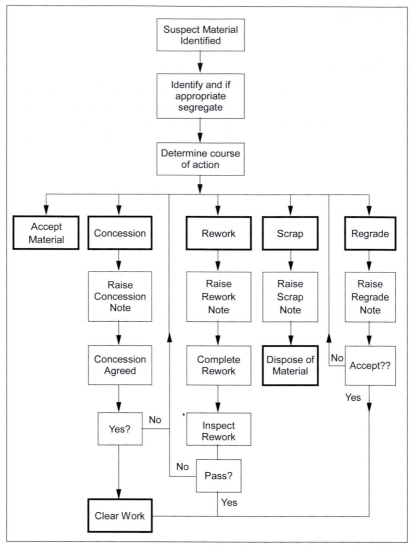

**Figure 20**  Control of Non-Conforming Product

## Types of Inspection

### *Inspection by attributes*

If inspection is limited to deciding whether an item is acceptable or not, then the form of inspection is said to be by attributes, i.e. does the item have the desired attribute or not. Attributes data is derived by counting the number or proportion of those items that do not have the desired attributes. Examples of inspection by attributes would be:

o      Use of a GO-NOGO[8] gauge

o      Subjective test as to acceptability of finish compared with a sample

o      Testing for leaks.

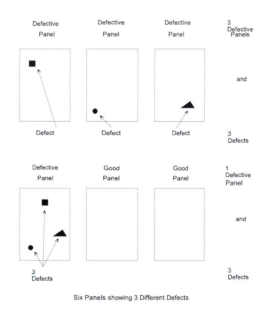

Six Panels showing 3 Different Defects

**Figure 21** Defectives or Defects. **Note:** An item may have three different flaws; in which case there are three **defects** in the item, but there is still only one **defective** item

---

8      A gauge having two settings one of which accepts components within the specified limits and one which does not accept components outside the specified limits.

# Types of Inspection

The statistical behaviour of attribute data is different from that of variable data and this must be taken into account when designing process control systems for attributes. To examine which type of data distribution is applicable, it is necessary to know something about the product form and attribute being inspected. The following classes lead to the use of different types of control chart which are based on different statistical distributions:

1. A product in discrete units each of which can be classified as acceptable or defective, e.g. ball bearings.

2. A product in discrete units which may possess a certain number of defects, e.g. a table top.

When a fixed sample from the first type of product is inspected, for example one hundred ball bearings, it is possible to state how many are defective. It is then possible to quickly work out how many are acceptable. So in this case, if two ball bearings are found to be defective (they can also be called 'non-conformities' or 'non-conforming items'), 98 will be acceptable. This is different to the second example. If a product is examined, such as a windscreen and found to have four defects - scratches or bubbles - it is not possible to make any statements about how many scratches/bubbles are not present. This type of defect data is similar to the number of goals scored in a football match. We can only report the number of goals scored, we are unable to report how many were not.

## *Inspection by variables*

Inspection methods that produce data that can be related to a scale such as linear dimensions, hardness, resistance, acidity etc. are referred to as inspection by variables. Obviously this data qualifies as continuous data. However, the natural limitations of the measuring instrument used will mean that the data has been grouped into discreet intervals. For instance, measurements are often to the nearest unit of measurement such as 0.01 mm or gramme.

Before proceeding, it would be useful to compare control by attributes to control by variables.

# Introduction to Quality

## *Advantages of using variables*

1. Small samples (e.g. five items) are sufficient to keep a check on both process average and variability.

2. Gradual changes such as drifts can be detected and the process reset *before* it goes out of specification limit. Changes in variability can be detected on the range chart.

3. Sudden changes in process average and variability can also be detected, but where this results in all work being out of specification limit, attributes will do this equally well.

## *Advantages of using attributes*

1. Many qualities cannot be measured conveniently as variables, e.g. appearance, taste etc, although some attributes, for example sweetness, are often estimated on a scale of say 0 to 5.

2. Attributes are usually easier to check and require a less skilled inspector.

3. Several types of defectives can be observed and plotted together as the total number rejected, but the chart should always include an analysis, so that types which often occur can be identified and investigated.

4. Sample sizes for attributes are much larger than for variables. For example, if the scrap from a process averages 1%, a sample of 100 is needed to have an average chance of finding one reject in it and rather more to give a good chance of doing so. Samples can, and sometimes are, taken specifically to provide data for an attribute chart, but in the majority of cases we use data from 100% inspection which is being performed anyway.

## Quality Control Strategy

*Introduction:* It can be seen from previous chapters that the modern approach towards Quality Assurance is the preventive approach. This involves anticipating and preparing for a right first time result.

*Development and Identification of the Quality Control Strategy*

This section discusses the Quality Control issues associated with various processes and attempts to develop a suitable Quality Control Strategy for each process type. Below are listed some possible scenarios that may require a Quality Control Strategy to be developed:

1.    A Batch Process - Where items of a similar type are collected into packets or batches of work for processing through the various process stages. For example, batches of say 20 components travelling around the various stages in a machine shop; batches of orders to process through the sales and then invoicing departments; batches of students to be processed through their various course stages and lectures.

2.    A Flow Process - A continuous process of manufacture. For example, an oil refinery, food or paint production.

3.    An Assembly Process - The assembly of an item from various sub-assemblies or parts. For example, car, computer, a piece of capital equipment. Here it is important to draw a distinction between Mass Production Assembly (a motor vehicle) and one off assemblies (an oil rig).

4.    A Service Process - The provision of assistance or aid. For example, bank, hospital, hotel, repair and maintenance, software support, etc.

5.    A Design Process - The process of researching, developing and designing a product or service. For example, design of a motor vehicle, an oil rig, a training course.

# Introduction to Quality

Each of the above process types would require the development of an appropriate Quality Control Strategy. There are many models that can be used for the purpose of this. ISO 9001 or ISO 9004 could be used as a general model; Guides to Good Laboratory Practice (GLP)or Good Manufacturing Practice (GMP) for the medical or food industry; QS 9000 or ISO TS 16949 for mass production, automobile or assembly processes and Boeing's D1 9000 for the Aerospace or capital equipment process.

The following is a simple strategy based on the approach presented by Caplen[9], namely, start right, keep right and finish right. Now, Caplen's model may be too simplistic when applied to very large organisations or processes. However, it has proved to be a very useful tool in circumstances where there is not a directly applicable model or when evaluating (for quality control purposes) short or small businesses processes. In manufacturing industries the idea of start right, keep right and finish right may be seen as first-off, patrol and last-off inspection. When the quality control strategy has been determined, then Inspection Planning (see page 68) has a role to play in finalising the overall approach.

For the purpose of illustration we shall now repeat and apply the principles of preventive control referred to in Part A. The following sets out the strategy for a typical manufacturing situation. This is followed by examples of application in other situations including service processes.

## Step 1   Start Right

o    Check that the operator, machine, tools etc. are capable with respect to the specified tolerance

o    Check instructions, drawings and documentation are available and at the right issue

o    Set up the machine

o    Inspect the first off

o    If the first-off is not within tolerance readjust the machine and repeat until correct.

---

[9]    R.H.Cpalen - "A practical approach to Quality Control"

**Step 2  Keep Right**

o  Inspect samples at suitable intervals

o  Plot inspection results on control charts

o  Interpret control chart and take corrective action when necessary.


**Step 3  Finish Right**

o  Inspect the last item and plot on the chart

o  Complete records and return documentation

o  Protect components for transport to the next stage

o  Return tools for refurbishment and safe storage

o  Carry out any planned maintenance.


The benefits of this approach are:

o  Manufacture of defective items is avoided

o  Defective work is prevented and, therefore, does not result in field failures

o  Increased manufacturing efficiency and profitability.

## Quality Control Strategy for Batch Processes

*Batch process - Start Right*. This entails ensuring that all the correct documentation, equipment, material and people are established before the process is run. The correct documentation includes the process method, instructions and specification (target values and tolerances) and inspection schedule; the tooling and equipment is of an adequate standard (see section on process capability studies); that the raw materials to be processed are from a qualified source (see section on supplier selection); that the personnel running the process are adequately trained and qualified.

One way of showing that personnel are adequately trained is by using a Training Matrix which shows the training status of the personnel. These matrices can also be reviewed by supervision during any training appraisal, and if appropriate, further or new training can be given to the staff. The example below shows a training matrix for a particular process.

| Process Name | Filling | | | |
|---|---|---|---|---|
| Process Owner | J Smith | | | |
| Person  Name | Person A | Person B | Person C | Person N |
| Stars | *** | * | **** | ***** |
| Task Name | | | | |
| Task 1 | A | B | C | D |
| Task 2 | D | C | B | A |
| Task 3 | A | A | A | A |
| Task n | B | B | B | B |

Five Star Training. The stars show the level of competence of each operator, for the particular process. There could be other Training Matrices for other processes. The stars associated with each person are process based and indicate:

*****     Able to teach the process; self inspect; set up; complete the process without supervision.

****     Able to complete the process; self inspect; set up with supervisor check off.

***     Limited experience, can complete the process but with supervision check off.

**     Very limited or no experience, can complete the process but with supervision.

*     Received induction, understands health and safety.

# Quality Control Strategy

The letters are task based and are associated with person and task. These letters indicate:

A       *Able to teach the process; self inspect; set up; complete the process without supervision.*

B       *Able to complete the process; self inspect; set up with supervisor check off.*

C       *Limited experience, can complete the process but with supervision check off.*

D       *Very limited or no experience, can complete the process but with supervision.*

E       *Received induction, understands health and safety.*

Before the process run, first-off- inspection may be required. Note, first-off-inspection does not necessarily mean it has to be performed by an inspector (more often this will be an operator). The role of the inspector may be to complete an audit of the first off process. Once the first off has satisfactorily passed inspection the route card will probably be up-dated for inspection status purposes.

**Table 4** 1st - off Inspection Audit Check List

| Process Name: | | |
|---|---|---|
| Batch No: | | |
| # | Check | Result |
| 1 | Is the quality standard adequately defined? | |
| 2 | Is the quality standard achievable? | |
| 3 | Is all documentation (process, inspection, routing, etc.) available? | |
| 4 | Are correct gauges, tools and equipment available? | |
| 5 | Has the operator been trained? | |
| 6 | Are the process controls set correctly? | |

*Batch process - Keep Right.* This should be the inspection schedule in action. Note again inspection does not necessarily mean it has to be performed by an inspector (more often this will be an operator). The inspection schedule may detail for each process stage:

**Table 5** Patrol Inspection Audit Check List

| Process Name: | | |
|---|---|---|
| Batch No | | |
| # | Check | Result |
| 1 | Are the operator checks being performed correctly? | |
| 2 | Are the records being maintained? | |
| 3 | Is corrective action being taken when required? | |
| 4 | Is the work adequately segregated and identified? | |

o    The features to be checked (together with target and tolerances)

o    The inspection equipment to be used

o    The frequency of inspection

o    The recording method (see Section on Control Charts).

The Inspector's role may be to audit that the operator checks are being performed correctly and recorded.  See Table - Patrol Inspection Audit Check List.

# Quality Control Strategy

*Batch process - Finish Right.* This stage could consist of completion of a last-off which may be a 100% or sample check of the completed batch items. However, this check should be unnecessary if the operator checks have been performed correctly.

**Table 6** Last - off Inspection Audit Check List

| Process Name: | | |
|---|---|---|
| Batch No | | |
| # | Check | Result |
| 1 | Have the final checks been correctly performed? | |
| 2 | Have all the records been completed? | |
| 3 | Has all the work been correctly identified and any rejects adequately segregated? | |
| 4 | If rejects have been made, has the appropriate corrective action been identified? | |
| 5 | Is the product adequately protected? | |
| 6 | Are all the gauges, tooling, equipment in a satisfactory condition? | |

# Introduction to Quality

## Quality Control Strategy for Flow Process

*Flow process - Start Right.* With a continuous process one of the key issues is that it is possible to make a considerable amount of product before a problem is discovered. For example, an oil refinery or a company making soup. It is, therefore, essential that the start right and keep right principles are adhered to, as finish right will only indicate that there is a major problem. (It may, however, be of some comfort to know this is one problem which, hopefully, will not reach the customer.)

Activities associated with applying starting right to flow processes could be quality planning and a detailed check of the process set up. Environmental issues may also be worthy of consideration. With specific reference to food production, cleanliness and hygiene for people, equipment and buildings will need to have been addressed. Issues such as pest control, building and equipment maintenance, and reliability become of paramount importance.

*Flow process - Keep Right.* Generally this will consist of monitoring checks of the process output by the laboratory, equipment process setting and parameter monitoring, either remotely or by the machine operator. The application of statistical process control (SPC) is particularly useful here.

*Flow process - Finish Right.* Final over-check of samples by the laboratory, analysis of SPC charts to identify any assignable causes of variation that might give a lead to process improvement.

## Quality Control Strategy for Assembly Process

*Assembly process - Start Right.* One of the key issues associated with Quality Control of the assembly process is that it is often not possible to know if the assembly will work until tested and, even then, reliability of the assembly cannot always be guaranteed until used by the customer. These two issues again indicate the importance of starting and keeping right rather than just finishing right. However, the final test is of importance to avoid installation, commissioning and warranty problems.

In the mass production industry, great effort is place on Starting Right. Control of supplied material is essential if the assembly process is going to continue to work efficiently and effectively. (See section Sub-contractor Quality Assurance page 132)

*Assembly process - Keep Right.* Consideration also needs to be given to the economics of the assembly tools with specific reference to fool proofing or Poka Yoke[10].

There are a number of different classifications of errors just as there are a number of different classifications of defects. (See page 65 Inspection Errors). It is important to understand the distinction between these differing types of errors and defects to determine the approach to eliminating or avoiding them. Eliminating the errors can involve a fool proof method, avoiding errors may require a specific inspection approach.

With Poka Yoke there are a number of approaches to avoiding errors. For example, some methods of avoiding human errors could be:

o      Location pins which only allow the assembly to be built in the correct orientation

o      Visual or audible alarms when items are misplaced or incorrectly positioned

o      Limit switches which stop machine operation if components are not correctly positioned

o      Stops or counters which clearly identify an incorrect attribute e.g. weight or size

o      Check lists to aid or remind operators. (Would you want to fly on a plane in which the pilot has not completed their pre-flight check list?)

---

[10] *Poka Yoke*      Shigeo Shingo "Poka Yoke"

# Introduction to Quality

The process of completing a poka-yoke exercise would be to:

    a.       Build quality into the process from the start

    b.       Build a team to:

           i.       Identify the sources of defects

           ii.      Identify the sources of error

           iii.     Determine a suitable solution

           iv.     Implement and test the solution.

*Assembly process - Finish Right.* Final testing of the product to ensure that the product in all respects complies with the customer and legal requirements. The final test specification and instruction needs to focus on the functional aspects of the product rather than any individual features of each assembly.

The test specification could include:

    a.       A statement of requirements for the finished product covering:

           i.       Equipment (Visual)

- Mechanical
- Electrical
- etc

           ii.      Equipment (Functional)

- Free cycling (not producing)
- Simulating actual condition of use
- Actual condition of use
- Health and safety
- External standards

# Quality Control Strategy

b.     The type of control chart to be used to record the results of the test could include:

- The test to be performed, see above list

- The target and tolerances to be achieved

- The frequency with which the measurement should be taken, i.e. if the test is of a piece of capital equipment, how frequently should the equipment performance be measured? Measuring this capital equipment performance also provides an opportunity to determine the reliability of the equipment, i.e. how often does the fitter need to adjust or repair the equipment, to maintain its performance?

- The sample size that needs to be taken.

- The duration of the test - as suggested above this needs to be of a duration that will provide adequate levels of confidence in the reliability of the equipment.

- If control charts are to be employed then the recording method will need to be established (attribute or variable charts).

# Introduction to Quality

## Quality Control Strategy for Service Processes

*Service process - Start Right.* In service organisations this usually means determining and specifying the customers' requirements. Not having a clear understanding of the customers' requirements is one the most significant causes of quality failure. In a hospital or bank a clear understanding of customer requirements may be stated in their mission statement or quality goal.

If one takes a motor vehicle garage which maintains and repairs motor vehicles as an example of a service process, then their control of Starting Right may consist of a statement regarding the range of vehicles they are capable of maintaining and a booking procedure that clearly identifies the customer needs.

Other aspects that will require controlling at this stage will include a service manual, garage equipment and personnel in terms of their training.

*Service process - Keep Right.* In the example used of a garage, the technicians will be following the manufacturers' recommendations regarding the repair, maintenance and testing of the vehicles. Their training and experience should also ensure that the correct inspections are performed.

These checks performed by the technicians could be augmented by regular supervisor audits. These audits would confirm the quality of the work and that the technician is observing the prescribed procedures.

One of the techniques employed by service industries to maintain the appropriate standards is the 5S approach.

*Introduction to 5S*: The 5S is a systematic approach to establishing and maintaining housekeeping standards. With this method, divisions or departments within organisations adopt and implement their own housekeeping programme, used as a means of improving quality, safety and productivity.

# Quality Control Strategy

*The 5S Programme:* This programme is based on the Japanese 5S Housekeeping programme[11] which has been successfully adopted in a number of organisations. Although originally the programme was mainly applied to manufacturing organisations, the programme has relevance to service organisations as well. Below is an interpretation of the 5S programme for a service organisation. The 5S's referred to are based on the Japanese words:

○      Seiri or Sorting (clearing out or arranging)

○      Seiton or Simplifying (configuring or tidying)

○      Seiso or Sweeping (cleaning)

○      Seiketsu or Standardising (clean condition or cleanliness)

○      Shitsuke or Self Discipline (culture, training or breeding).

The benefits in an office environment are that this approach has the potential to reduce the number of ledgers, forms and documents. It can improve file retrieval and archiving times. Possibly and most importantly, it provides a catalyst for team building and office process improvement. Offices often provide the customer with their first impression of the organisation and this may reflect (in the customer's view), our approach to work.

The overall aim is to encourage a *"one is best"* campaign of the office: one item of equipment, one file and one filing system, one-page memos, one-hour meetings, one -minute telephone calls, one-day processing.

**Seiri** or sorting (Clearing out or arranging)

This refers to clearing out anything and everything that is not required in the workplace. Photographs (coloured with photograph dates) can be taken of the workplace before starting the clearing out process. This is to bench mark or identify the current status in order to show what improvements have been made. A tagging system can be used by the personnel responsible for the area to identify any items or documents not directly involved with their work place or surrounding area.

---

[11]      Samuel K Ho - TQM An Integrated Approach

# Introduction to Quality

**Seiton** or simplifying (Configuring or tidying)

The tasks or activity area needs to be organised or configured in order to ensure that items are located correctly and can be easily found. Every desk and storage area could have its own address. In this way the whole area can then be organised into an address grid. The various work areas, desks, copying, stores, cabinets, etc. could be (colour) coded.

**Seiso** or sweeping (Cleaning)

The purpose of cleaning is to maintain the workplace in a suitable condition for the activities and tasks that need to be performed. This is achieved by ensuring that all excess material or documentation is suitably located or disposed of. All areas that have to be cleaned should be clearly identified with responsibilities allocated and frequency pre-determined.

**Seiketsu** or standardising (Clean condition or cleanliness)

The work area needs to be maintained in a clean and tidy condition at all times, with no accumulation of unnecessary items or documentation.

**Shitsuke** or self discipline (Culture, training or breeding)

A working environment needs to be created that welcomes constructive criticism and an improvement culture. This environment is essential if problem points are to be quickly and easily identified and rectified. All work areas need to be clean and tidy, and free of unnecessary materials and products. Only machines, tools, instruments and equipment which are actually used shall be in place. There should be techniques for removing unnecessary items. Work areas should be organised and all machines/equipment labelled and easily identified. All stored and necessary items should be immediately visible. Maximum and minimum stock levels of consumables need to be clearly visible. All work areas and passage ways should be clearly separated. The storage location of tools/instruments should be clearly labelled for ease of operation and return. The work place should be free of dirt, spills, clothing and other extraneous materials. All machines, tools, equipment and containers should be clean and in good condition. Responsibilities for cleaning and the state of items should be allocated and cleaning should be a regular part of work. The work place should be standardised and there should be a system for regular clearing up, organising and cleaning. There should be training and discipline in housekeeping. All staff should be aware of procedures and all procedures strictly followed. All housekeeping actions

# Quality Control Strategy

should be taken promptly and all actions and controls should be effective. Audits should be conducted against housekeeping procedures.

All Shitsuke should be practised until it has become natural habit.

Detailed below is a check list which could be employed when conducting a 5S assessment.

| 5S Check List | | | Section: . . . . . . . . . . . . . . . | Checker: . . . . . | | | | |
|---|---|---|---|---|---|---|---|---|---|
| Marks: . . . . . . . . . . . . . . . % | | | Previous Marks: . . . . . . . % | Date: . . . . . . . | | | | | |
| 5S | # | Checking Item | Evaluation Criteria | 0 | 1 | 2 | 3 | 4 |
| Clearing Up (20 Marks) | 1 | Task inputs & Deliverables | No unnecessary paper work or finished documentation left lying around. | | | | | |
| | 2 | Equipment (utilisation) | All equipment is in regular use. | | | | | |
| | 3 | Equipment (condition) | All equipment is regularly serviced & maintained. | | | | | |
| | 4 | Visual control | There are no unnecessary items left lying around on tops of desks, cabinets or chairs. | | | | | |
| | 5 | Standards for disposal | Items and documentation are properly disposed of, e.g. tag items. | | | | | |

# Quality Control Strategy

| 5S | # | Checking Item | Evaluation Criteria | 0 | 1 | 2 | 3 | 4 |
|---|---|---|---|---|---|---|---|---|
| Organising (20 Marks) | 1 | Equipment labelling | Equipment is clearly labelled. | | | | | |
| | 2 | Necessary items | All necessary items can be quickly identified and located. | | | | | |
| | 3 | Consumables | Minimum and maximum stock levels are established and visible. | | | | | |
| | 4 | Dividing lines | Work areas and passageways are clearly divided. | | | | | |
| | 5 | Equipment and tools | Storage locations of tools and equipment are clearly marked for ease of use and return. | | | | | |
| Cleaning (20 marks) | 1 | Floors | Clean and clear. | | | | | |
| | 2 | Equipment | Tidy and serviceable. | | | | | |
| | 3 | Desks and cabinets | Clear and tidy. | | | | | |
| | 4 | Computers and ancillaries | Tidy and serviceable. | | | | | |
| | 5 | Health and safety | Fire, protective equipment, lifting & handling, COSHH, disaster recovery. | | | | | |
| Standardising (20 Marks) | 1 | One method of working, e.g. one day processing | Process based procedures available. Targets set and records kept of processing performance. | | | | | |
| | 2 | One set of files, e.g. one location, one copy, one minute file storage and retrieval | Examine file condition Test ability to store and retrieve records in one minute. | | | | | |

| 5S | # | Checking Item | Evaluation Criteria | 0 | 1 | 2 | 3 | 4 |
|---|---|---|---|---|---|---|---|---|
| | 3 | One set of documentation e.g. forms and one-page memos | Examine forms. Examine memos. | | | | | |
| | 4 | One piece of equipment | Examine equipment availability and quantity. | | | | | |
| | 5 | One-minute telephone calls, one-hour meetings, | Review telephone call practice and duration. Review meeting times. | | | | | |
| Training & Discipline (20 Marks) | 1 | 5S Programme and audit results | Result published, reviewed and improvements made. | | | | | |
| | 2 | Team building | Process improvement. Meetings held and real solutions identified. | | | | | |
| | 3 | Team briefing and communication | Team briefing held. | | | | | |
| | 4 | Absenteeism and employee turn over | Review records. | | | | | |
| | 5 | Recognition | Recognition for achievement is observed. | | | | | |
| Total | | | | | | | | |

Key

| Scores | |
|---|---|
| 0 | Very Poor |
| 1 | Poor |
| 2 | Average |
| 3 | Good |
| 4 | Very Good |

## Quality Control Strategy

These audit check lists could be reviewed and analysed at a pre-determined frequency to show the improvements made.

*Service Process - Finish Right.* To return to the example of the motor vehicle garage, once all the maintenance and repairs have been completed and before the work sheet is signed off, the vehicle would need to be road tested. This confirms that the vehicle has been safely repaired and that there are no other unreported faults.

The use of a reply card could possibly be left for the business to gauge customer reaction to the quality of the service provided.

## Quality Control Strategy for Design Processes

*Design process - Start Right*. The design or project control process. (See section on Design Control). Initially it is important to have established project and design procedures and codes of practice, so that a clear statement of working practices is defined. These procedures need to address the establishment of the customer's requirements including issues such as document control, specification assurance, document validation and verification methods and project sizing. Once the project has been established then the project risks can be established by the use of risk analysis techniques such as: Failure Mode Effect and Criticality Analysis, Fault Tree Analysis, etc. With the potential risk understood, project and quality planning can be completed. The risk analysis should provide information regarding the potential risk to the project and the quality plan should deal with, amongst other things, the way in which these risks will be addressed, minimised or eliminated. The quality plan could also include the timing of the project audits.

*Design process - Keep Right*. With the project under way, project records should be established and created. These will need to include records of configuration management. Part of keeping the project or design right can be approvals of documentation, e.g. drawings and calculation, reviews and monitoring (e.g. cost, specification, time and health and safety). The results of any project audits should also be available for corrective action and closed down.

*Design process - Finish Right*. At the conclusion of the design or project, a validation of project deliverables should be completed. This will ensure that the project complies with and addresses customer requirements.

# Part 2


# Standardising Organisations

# Introduction to Quality

## Standardising Organisations

## Introduction

In this section, an overview of some of the relevant certification schemes, standards and guides, and quality-related bodies is presented. It is not intended to be exhaustive, but merely to introduce the more common ones.

## Company, Industrial and National Standards

In addition to the public standards described below, most manufacturing industries also have extensive internal standards. For example, there are British Standards for a huge range of goods, agreed over the years by the relevant industry bodies. The European Union has also set hundreds of mandatory product standards for goods affecting health, safety and the environment, as described in a later section.

Most individual manufacturers will also have comprehensive production plans for each product they manufacture. These plans are at least the equivalent of internal standards, and typically cover every aspect of the production process.

These plans might include any or all of the following:

- o product design
- o key product and process quality criteria
- o machine and production line set-up
- o controls and settings
- o raw materials requirements and standards
- o processing instructions and methods
- o in-process and final monitoring, testing methods and criteria
- o product identification and traceability, requirements and methods
- o packaging
- o storage, handling and delivery handling requirements.

## Standardising Organisations

Company standards are normally maintained by a central group (e.g. the quality department or drawing office) and are based on a combination of public standards and the technology and management methods that the company will actually use to make the products. For the same reasons, control and enforcement of internal standards is just as important as control and enforcement of public standards. No one in the whole organisation has enough knowledge or experience of all the factors affecting the product to be able to change the standard at will, and variations should only be allowed with full consultation, approval and only under properly controlled conditions.

Company and industry standards are much less the norm in service companies. This is partly because services are perceived much more as a matter of personal skill and experience. This is partly because the quality of the service is judged by more subjective criteria, and partly because the culture of objective standards has yet to mature in this environment. The same is largely true of IT, R&D organisations and government departments.

## Approval and Certification Schemes

An approval or certification scheme implies that someone is approving someone else against an agreed standard. There are basically two types of standard. One applies to management systems as a whole, the other applies more specifically to products or processes. One of the first major approving bodies in the UK was the British Standards Institute (BSI) although there are now many others that specialise in specific areas.

Certification invariably means that the firm seeking certification must establish documented systems of Quality Control which satisfy the requirements of the relevant standard. This usually requires the systems and processes to be documented. Once documented, the systems and activities in operation should comply with these documented arrangements. This is verified by appropriate external and internal audits. Once a firm is approved, periodic audits are carried out to verify that the firm is continuing to comply.

**Certification Schemes for Quality Systems**

*Quality Management System (QMS) - The management of quality*

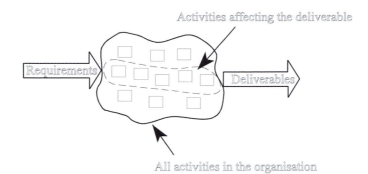

**Figure 22** The Scope of the Application of a QMS

The scope of the application of a Quality Management System (QMS) must be clearly defined.

Typically, activities excluded from a QMS are occupational health and safety at work, environmental issues, personnel functions other than training, internal finance, accounting and marketing.

Quality System Standards apply only to the quality processes. They do not specify product or service grades. These are set either by other standards or codes of practice pertinent to the industry, or by the customer or by the supplier. For example:

- o  Legislation e.g. safety regulations

- o  British Standards (or equivalent) for products and Codes of Practice

- o  Customer specifications

- o  Supplier specifications.

# Standardising Organisations

## ISO 9000[12]

This standard specifies the requirements for a general Quality Management System. It is not intended to be a company specific quality standard, but a practical standard for quality systems which can be applied to any industry.

The principles of ISO 9000 are applicable regardless of the size of the firm. It identifies the basic disciplines and specifies the shape of a management quality assurance system to ensure that the supplier meets the customer requirements.

## ISO 9001

ISO 9000 is an internationally recognised standard and is simply 'common sense' set down on paper in an organised way. The standard comprises a number of requirements which firms must address to gain certification. Depending on the scope of operation of the firm, some of the requirements may not be applicable. While the standard specifies what activities need to be addressed, it does not say how. Most successful firms are already applying the underlying principles embodied in ISO 9001. However, often the quality systems may not be fully documented and there may not be records which confirm observance of the specified quality system.

Suppliers can use ISO 9001 as a guide when setting up their own systems.

Customers can specify ISO 9001 in the contract as a means of controlling the quality of goods and services they are purchasing. ISO 9001 may augment the customer's own product specific standards.

Third parties can use ISO 9001 as a basis for assessing a supplier's management system and, consequently, its ability to produce satisfactory goods and services. Firms successful in gaining a certificate are listed in the Department of Trade and Industry (DTI) Register of Firms of Assessed Capability.

---

[12]    Note; ISO 9000 is used here in the generic sense to refer to ISO 9001. See "The ISO 9000 family of Standards"

# Introduction to Quality

It should be noted that ISO 9001 does not specify the quality or standard of the delivered product or service. It does however, specify the quality of the system which produces the product or service. The quality standard of the product or service is prescribed by the purchaser and agreed by the supplier in a contract for the products or services. Requirements are prescribed by the supplier which are perceived as satisfying a market need.

The cost of achieving and maintaining certification status remains entirely with the firm seeking certification.

## Certification

There are a number of third party (independent) Accreditation bodies that provide a certification service which certificate organisations who have satisfied the Accreditation bodies' assessment criteria. If an ISO 9001 assessment (it could be other standards e.g ISO TS 16949) then the Accreditation body would confirm (certify) that the organisation has installed and operates a QMS in accordance with ISO 9001. This would afford the right for the certificated organisation to proclaim to all its key stakeholders, e.g customers, competitors, suppliers, etc. that they are an organisation of ISO 9001 assessed capability. If certification by BSI (or other accredited body) is intended, they will first carry out an assessment of the organisation comprising an adequacy audit on the Quality Manual followed by an initial compliance audit on site. Companies that qualify are registered in the DTI Register of Companies of Assessed Capability. After registration, surveillance audits will be carried out, usually twice a year, for as long as registration is maintained. Needless to say that all this is at the supplier's expense.

## What the standard is about

ISO 9001 is about managing and controlling quality rather than leaving things to chance. What this means is:

a. Commitment at the highest level that the organisation is serious about installing and maintaining a Quality Management System. This results in a Quality Policy Statement.

b. Analysing and agreeing the best way to ensure that all quality determinants are identified and controlled. Where existing methods of working are known to be effective and efficient, the aim should be to describe them as they are rather than trying to change everyone to work to new unknown methods.

c.  Allocating responsibilities for quality. Since quality is everyone's business, what this means in practice must be spelt out in writing. Otherwise, quality ends up being nobody's business. In particular, a management representative must be identified with the specific responsibility of maintaining the QMS and resolve any issues of conflict in relation to the attainment of quality.

d.  Documenting the arrangements for controlling quality. In addition to the Quality Manual and Procedures Manual, all other documentation relating to quality must be available and controlled to ensure its current status is at the correct issue. Since every organisation, and possibly every department in that organisation, will have its own customs and practice, the standard allows for each organisation to decide how it intends to address the requirements of the standard. Therefore, quality manuals and the supporting documented system will be unique to the organisation concerned. Much of the required documentation will already exist within the organisation, but because there is so much documentation it needs to be organised into a manageable form.

e.  Being able to demonstrate, usually through relevant records, that the system is being adhered to.

f.  Carrying out regular internal audits to identify and correct deviations from agreed procedures.

# Introduction to Quality

*The ISO 9000 family of standards*

Generally, ISO 9000 refers to a family of standards and guides related to the management of quality. There is ISO 9000, ISO 9001 and ISO 9004.

Specifically, **ISO 9000** comprises four parts as follows:

| | |
|---|---|
| ISO 9000-1:1994 | Quality management and quality assurance standards - Part 1: Guide to selection and use. |
| ISO 9000-2:1993 | Quality management and quality assurance standards - Part 2: Generic guidelines for the application of ISO 9001, ISO 9002 and ISO 9003. |
| ISO 9000-3:1991 | Quality management and quality assurance standards - Part 3: Guidelines for the application of ISO 9001 to the development, supply and maintenance of software. |
| ISO 9000-4:1994 | Quality management and quality assurance standards - Part 4: Guide to dependability programme management. |

Notice that these are all guides. However, ISO 9000-3 in particular is often used as though it were a standard.

ISO 9001 is a conformance standard. It specifies what must be done if an organisation wishes to obtain a certificate. This is the standard the certification body will use to assess an organisation's quality system. Only one of these standards will apply to an organisation depending on its scope of activities as follows:

| | |
|---|---|
| ISO 9001:2000 | Quality systems - Model for quality assurance in **design, development, production, installation and servicing.** |
| | (Formerly ISO 9001:1994 and BS 5750) |
| ISO 9004 | This is a set of guides intended to provide further clarification of the various aspects of the three compliance standards. |
| ISO 9004-1:1994 | Quality management and quality system elements - Part 1: Guidelines (Replaces BS 5750 Part 0 Section 0.2). |

| ISO 9004-2:1991 | Quality management and quality systems elements - Part 2: Guidelines for services. |
| ISO 9004-3:1993 | Quality management and quality systems elements - Part 3: Guidelines for processed materials. |
| ISO 9004-4:1993 | Quality management and quality systems elements - Part 4: Guidelines for quality improvement. |

It was originally intended that this list of guides should be extended as part of ISO 9004. However, some of them have now been published outside of the ISO 9000 family as follows:

| ISO 10005: | Quality management guidelines for quality plans. |
| ISO 10007: | Quality management guidelines for configuration management. |
| ISO 10011: | Guidelines for quality auditing. |
| ISO 10012: | Guidelines for measurement. |
| ISO 10013: | Guidelines for developing quality manuals. |

**Year 2000 ISO 9000 Product Line**

So what are these changes? First of all, the overall structure of the ISO 9000 family of standards and guides have been reduced to just three documents: ISO 9000, ISO 9001 and ISO 9004, supported by the ISO 10000 series of guides.

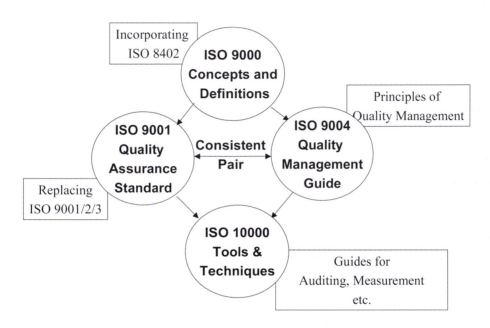

**Figure 23** Proposed year 2000 ISO 9000 Product Line
(Adapted from Fig 1 ISO/CD2 9001:2000)

ISO 9000 is the umbrella guide based on a revision of the current ISO 8402 glossary of terms used in Quality Assurance.

ISO 9001 replaces ISO 9001, ISO 9002 and ISO 9003 as the compliance standard for Quality Assurance. A company seeking registration will agree with the certification body which elements are applicable and which can be legitimately considered inapplicable.

# Standardising Organisations

ISO 9004 is a guide for Quality Management. It has been designed to be consistent with ISO 9001 but provides a much wider scope in the direction of Total Quality Management. ISO 9001 may be considered to be a subset of the new ISO 9004.

The ISO 10000 series is to be the repository of the guides for tools and techniques which may be applied in isolation or in support of ISO 9001/4.

## *Process based structure*

Returning to the structure and content of ISO 9001 and ISO 9004, all the elements of the current ISO 9001 are included and in many cases enhanced and/or with much greater clarification. However, the structure of the standard is based on what is considered to be a generic process model comprising four principal subsystems:

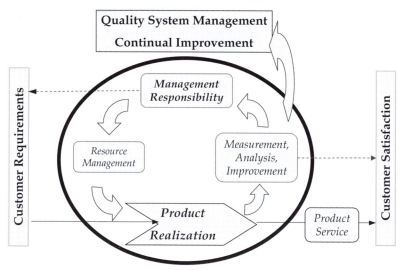

**Figure 24** Process based quality system (Adapted from Fig 1 ISO/CD2 9001:2000)

Management Responsibility - *requirements, policy, planning, management systems, responsibilities and review.*

Resource Management - *requirements, human resources, information, infrastructure and work environment.*

Product and/or service realisation - *customer related processes, design and development, purchasing, production and service operations, control of measuring and monitoring devices.*

Measurement, analysis and improvement - *Measurement and monitoring of system performance (auditing), customer satisfaction and processes, control of non-conformity, analysis of data and improvement.*

## Defence Standards (Def Stan's) and AQAPs

This was the forerunner of the British Standard and subsequently the ISO standard. However, it was essentially a second party approval scheme applicable to the Ministry of Defence and NATO contracts. Apart from some exceptional overseas contracts, the Allied Quality Assurance Publications (AQAP) have now been superseded with Def Stans 91, 92 and 93 which invoke the respective ISO standard.

As with ISO 9000 registered firms, there is a similar register of AQAP firms of assessed capability which is used as a basis for selecting MOD or NATO contractors. The appropriate level of ISO 9000 standard would be called up in the contract.

Where the customer carries out the assessment of the supplier, this is known as a second party assessment. Unlike third party assessments, such as those carried out by BSI, the costs of initial and subsequent re-assessments are borne by the purchaser, i.e. MOD or NATO. In addition, primary contracts are allocated a Quality Assurance Representative (QAR) who monitors that the terms of the contract are adhered to, including compliance with the relevant quality system standard.

# Product Standards & Certification

## Product Standards and Certification

### BSI Kitemark

The British Standard Kitemark is a registered trade mark owned by BSI and may only be used by manufacturers licensed by BSI under a particular Kitemark scheme. The appearance of this distinctive symbol on a product indicates that BSI has independently tested samples of the product against the appropriate British Standard and confirmed that the standard has been complied with in every respect. There are a number of different types of standards:

- Quality Management System standard, e.g. ISO 9001, is a model for a Quality Management System.

- Product standards, e.g. BS 1363, is a specification for 13 amp electrical plugs.

- Non product related standards, e.g BS 4500 for limits and fits, BS EN ISO for 1660 dimensioning and tolerancing of profiles, BS 308 for technical drawings.

The Kitemark is in reference to a product standard, indicating that samples of the product have been tested and conform with the particular British or International Standard. Placing reference to this standard e.g. BS 1363, means that the manufacturer is indicating that the product in all respects conforms to the requirements of that particular standard. Using the Kitemark warrants that BSI has confirmed that tested samples of the product have the ability to meet this standard. In certain circumstances the manufacturer will also be required to produce and maintain a Quality System based on ISO 9000 'Quality Systems'. This Quality System will be assessed as part of the certification process and should set out the organisation, responsibilities, procedures and methods involved in manufacturing the product. BSI is not the only body providing this service, many other organisations will provide product certification and approval:

- BEAB is one of the leading bodies for the approval of domestic electrotechnical products in the UK

- BASEC, the British Approvals Service for Cables.

## BSI Safety Mark

This mark appears on products which have safety related issues or requirements and where there is a recognised and accepted safety standard associated with the product. The safety mark warrants that the product complies in all respects with the standard and, furthermore, (in the case of BSI Safety Mark) this has been confirmed by BSI. These products can include domestic gas equipment (cooker, boilers, gas fires), floodlights, electrical plugs, crash helmets, etc. As with the Kitemark, the Safety Mark can only be used by manufacturers licensed under a Safety Mark scheme, which involves an assessment procedure similar to that of the Kitemark. Certain products, e.g. motorcycle helmets must be sold with some form of safety mark. Again, it is worth noting that BSI are not the only Safety Certification Body.

Other inspectorates/certification bodies: there are now over sixty accredited organisations who grant certification to the companies who conform to ISO 9001. In addition, there are a number of industry specific standards set by certain industries. These include:

- CAA - Civil Aviation Authority
- PVQAB - Pressure Vessels Quality Assurance Board
- CEGB - BS 5882 QA Nuclear
- DHSS - Good Manufacturing Practices/Good Laboratory Practices applicable in the medical industry and other situations where hygiene is of special importance.

## EU Notified Bodies

Notified Bodies are organisations identified by the national governments of the member states as being competent to make independent judgments about whether or not a product complies with the essential safety requirements laid down by each CE marking directive. To become a Notified Body, the management must fulfill certain conditions. This includes defining the scope of its notified activities, which must be given ('notified') to the European Commission. See Section on CE Marking.

*Certification Bodies*

**Accreditation of Certification Bodies**

Apart from approval schemes, there are a number of national bodies which offer services in the field of quality. The standards of these services are in turn controlled and maintained to nationally agreed criteria.

The United Kingdom Accreditation Service (UKAS) operates accreditation schemes for Certification Bodies. These are National Accreditation of Certification Bodies (NACB) for the accreditation of Certification Bodies, and the National Assessment and Measurement Accreditation Service (NAMAS) for accreditation of Calibration Laboratories or Test Houses. NACB use EN 45000 series to accredit Certification Bodies who certify organisations using the ISO 9000 series of standards. NAMAS use EN 45001 (M10) as the basis for their accreditation.

Diagrammatically the hierarchy of these bodies would be as shown in **Figure 25**.

*The National Accreditation of Certification Bodies (NACB)*

The NACB operates a system of accreditation of Certification Bodies such as BSI, Lloyds, Bureau Veritas Quality

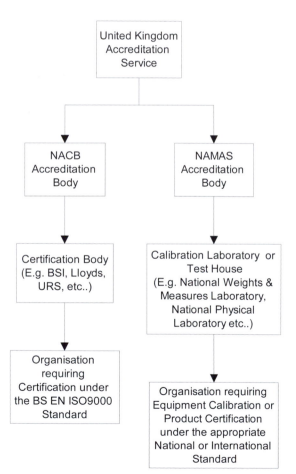

**Figure 25** Accreditation Bodies

International, United Register of Systems etc. who certify organisations using the ISO 9000 series.

The purpose of NACB is to assess the independence and technical competence of UK certification bodies to the requirements of EN 45011/2/3.

o   EN 45011 is the standard for certification bodies when issuing certificates of product conformity

o   EN 45012 is the standard for the certification bodies' own Quality Management System usually based on ISO 9001, i.e. the Certification Bodies Quality Manual, Quality Manager, Internal Audit procedure etc.

o   EN 45013 is used to assess the competence of the certification bodies' own personnel (assessors).

Together, these standards cover the structure, operation and management of the certification body.

Once the certification body is accredited, it is granted the right to use the Tick and Crown symbol. This symbol denotes that the certification body has been accredited in a particular industrial sector. Not all certification bodies are accredited in all industrial sectors. For example, some certification bodies are not accredited by the NACB in the medical or software sectors. In this situation, certification bodies may still assess and issue certificates to companies working in the medical and software industrial sectors. However, the certificates issued cannot carry the Tick and Crown.

**Figure 26**

The accreditation process is very similar to the ISO 9001 certification process with application, pre-assessment, adequacy audit, full assessment and, if successful, accreditation.

## Certification Bodies

Once a certification body is accredited by the NACB, then any organisations certificated by that body can appear in the DTI QA register of approved companies, together with the certification bodies' own guide, e.g. BSI Buyers Guide.

### *The national assessment and measurement accreditation service (NAMAS)*

The purpose of NAMAS, the National Assessment and Measurement Accreditation Service, is to assess, accredit and monitor test houses and calibration laboratories. The value of this accreditation is based on the need to ensure that products are produced to specification and that products are safe. Note: product certification not management system certification. NAMAS accredited laboratories can provide this necessary assurance of the competence of calibration and testing houses. It is this competence which will avoid the need for multiple assessment of calibration and testing laboratories. NAMAS certificates of calibration and test reports have now been recognised by organisations such as British Telecom, Ministry of Defence, Rolls Royce etc. NAMAS are also involved with gaining agreement on the recognition of other national schemes and as a consequence, international acceptance of the competence of the accredited laboratory.

Following the stringent examination to the requirements usually of the standards M10 and M11[13], laboratories would then be authorised to use the formal certification and reports to record the results of any measurements and tests taken. These standards are very similar to ISO 9001 but with reference to calibration.

The method of certification is also very similar to the approach that would be adopted by the NACB or any other accreditation body. There is an application. The laboratory documentation is examined. There is a pre-assessment and then a full assessment of the laboratory.

Any non-compliance to M10 and M11 would then be reported. If any were found, corrective action would be taken and on satisfactory completion of these corrective actions NAMAS would offer the laboratory accreditation. The NAMAS certificate

---

[13] M10 & M11 are similar to BS 7500 series, EN 45001 & EN 45002 and ISO Guides 25 & 54. These documents cover the accreditation standard and regulations for measurement and calibration facilities.

would then be issued and the surveillance visits would then commence on a regular basis. Once certificated the accredited laboratory services would be publicised through the NAMAS directory of accredited laboratories.

These accredited laboratories can include commercial calibration laboratories and test houses as well as laboratories forming part of larger organisations such as a manufacturing company, university, or some government organisation.

Only laboratories accredited by NAMAS may use the NAMAS logo in conjunction with their accreditation number. This is an important distinction and one which is carefully guarded by NAMAS to the extent that forging of these NAMAS certificates has resulted in custodial sentences for the misuse of these certificates.

A typical example of one of these NAMAS certificated reports is shown in **Figure 27**.

# Certification Bodies

## Figure 27 Typical Calibration Certificate

---

### CERTIFICATE OF CALIBRATION
Issued by Quality Management & Training Laboratory

**Date of Issue: 13 July 1995**          **Serial No: 1234**

**NAMAS**

---

| | |
|---|---|
| Quality Management & Training Laboratory | **CALIBRATION NO:** |
| P O Box No 172 | **Approved Signatories** |
| Guildford Surrey GU2 7FN | Mr F Tickle BA CEng MIMechE MIEE MIQA |
| Tel: 01483 453511 | Signed **F Tickle** |
| **Page 1 of 1 pages** | Mr G Vorley MSc MIQA  Signed **G Vorley** |

---

CUSTOMER:                  Vakes Ltd Benley Park Guildford

DESCRIPTION:               1 off Micrometer to measure 0 to 25mm ± 0.01mm

SERIAL NO:                 12345

DATE OF CALIBRATION:       13 July 1995

### REPORT

BASIS OF TEST:             A specified tolerance of ±1%

DIMENSIONAL:               The gauge was measured for pressure at seven positions across the range of the equipment using the Butenburgh testing rig.  Serial No 123456.

The results were taken at 20°c +/- 2°c

| MEASURING POSITIONS | | RESULTS (mm) |
|---|---|---|
| 1 | 0 mm | 0 |
| 2 | 5 | 5.001 |
| 3 | 10 | 9.995 |
| 4 | 15 | 15.008 |
| 5 | 20 | 19.996 |

Uncertainty of measurement ± .5%

All measurement values were within the tolerance specified above

Signature **F Tickle**

The uncertainties are for a confidence probability of not less than 95%.

This certificate is issued in accordance with the conditions of the accreditation gained by the National Measurement Accreditation Services which has assessed the measuring capabilities of the laboratory and is traceable to recognised National Standards and for the units of measurements realised at the corresponding National Standards Laboratory.  Copyright of the certificate is jointly owned by the Crown and issuing Laboratory and may not be reproduced in full except with the prior written approval of head of NAMAS and the issuing laboratory.

# Part 3

# Total Involvement in Quality

## Total Involvement in Quality

### Justification of Quality Assurance Activities

*Why is quality assurance so important?*

There are a number of imperatives associated with quality assurance. Detailed below are what are considered to be the more important, namely:

o   Economic Imperative - The cost of poor quality and the opportunity for significant cost savings

o   Legal Imperative - The law associated with Quality Assurance both criminal and civil

o   Marketing Imperative - The competition and customer satisfaction

o   Survival Imperative - We live in a dangerous world. Can Quality Assurance provide some protection?

### *The Economic Imperative*

**Figure 29** illustrates the consequential cost of errors or changes introduced at various stages of the product cycle:

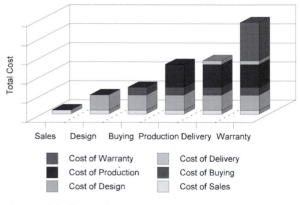

If an error is made at the sales stage and is discovered and corrected immediately, then the cost of the error is limited to the cost of re-working the sales process. If the error is not discovered until after the design stage, then the cost of the error

**Figure 29** Cost of Errors

includes not only re-working the sales process but also the design process. And so it goes on. If the error is not discovered until after delivery, then the costs to rectify the error may be enormous.

116

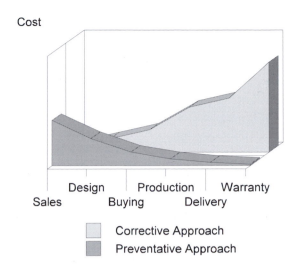

**Figure 30** illustrates the importance of preventing errors as early as possible. For this reason, the Japanese have turned the graph around and invest money at the front end to ensure that design errors are not fed into the cycle. This investment is far less than the costs of correction resulting from not investing.

**Figure 30** Benefits of Investing in Prevention

## *The Legal Imperative*

There are numerous examples of organisations being fined as a result of poor quality of products or services. Strict laws are now in place in the UK to protect the consumer, e.g. the Strict Liability law specifies that the immediate supplier of a product or service is liable for it being of satisfactory quality. The retailer cannot hide behind the fact that their supplier is to blame.

UK airline fined after sloppy work nearly caused crash

Builders to be sued over bungled library

BR braced for claims over faulty doors

# Total Involvement in Quality

## *The Marketing Imperative*

Unless an organisation is in a virtually monopolistic situation, it is going to have to watch its competitors very carefully to ensure that it can retain market share. The Japanese have demonstrated that quality and reliability sells. Their success can no longer be attributed to cheap labour costs but rather to the efficiency with which they have re-engineered products to be more reliable and cheaper.

Consider a company which has the lion's share of the market, say 30%. If its quality record is at the same level as its nearest competitor, company B, which has say 10% of the market, then in real terms A has three times the number of disappointed customers as B. Everyone knows someone who has a defective product from A. In other words, A has three times the exposure and must, therefore, be at least three times better.

The car industry provides good examples of this. Vauxhall in the mid 50s nearly went out of business; Lancia in the 80s lost most of their UK markets; Jaguar in the 70s and Rovers in the early 80's likewise.

What makes a customer chose one product over another? Well there are a number of factors that will influence the purchasing decision. **Figure 32** indicates four key factors:

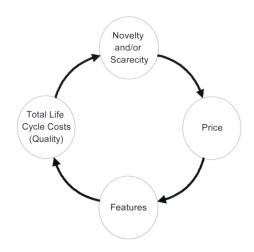

○ Novelty - Organisations need to develop a strategy for maintaining their products and services position in the market place

○ Price (value for money) - Organisations need to develop a strategy to become and maintain their position as lowest cost producer. Quality sells studies have shown that

**Figure 32** Purchasing Influences

customers will pay up to a 30% price premium if they consider the quality to be superior to the competitors o Features - Organisations need to develop a strategy to ensure that their products and services are continually upgraded to maintain their preeminent position

o Total life cost (quality, reliability, maintainability, etc.) - Customers do not just buy on the basis of price they also evaluate the life time cost of using the product or service.

*The Survival Imperative*

Today, as never before, society is virtually totally dependent on technology and quality failures frequently have catastrophic consequences. You only have to read the newspapers to begin to realise the world is a very dangerous place!

**Wiring technician made mistakes all his working life**

MR BRIAN HEMINGWAY

**GPs' sloppy handwriting 'still killing patients'**

**Slack accounting blamed for £85m training errors**

Slack accounting and administrative errors that led to more than £85 million being wrongly paid to trainees were attacked by the Commons Public Accounts Committee yesterday.

**Wrong drugs 'kill arthritis patients'**

*"Holiday jet battered by barrage of bricks -*

*A holiday jet carrying 145 passengers was seriously damaged by flying bricks as it took off from Luton airport last week. Thrust from the engine lifted paving slabs from the runway, throwing them up to strike tail stabiliser, causing damage."*

**'Meltdown' fear over accident at nuclear plant**

*"Wrong bolts held aircraft windscreen -*

*The windscreen of the British Airways BAC 1-11 airliner which blew out at 17,000 feet, sucking the captain half out of the cockpit was held in with the wrong bolts."*

*"Wiring technician made mistakes all his working life -*

*'Positively dangerous' working practices which caused the Clapham Junction rail disaster in which 35 people died. The report on the disaster revealed negligence at eleven levels of supervision and management."*

# Total Involvement in Quality

*"GPs' sloppy handwriting 'still killing patients' -*

*Inderal - for controlling high blood pressure - was mistaken for the asthma agent Intal. The patient died. An anaesthetics registrar injected what he thought was atropine - used before operations - and the patient had a fatal heart attack. The ampoule had contained adrenaline."*

*"Bolt change caused Chinook crash -*

*A comparatively minor design change introduced last year caused a vital gearbox component to fail catastrophically. Forty-five men died in the crash."*

This small selection should leave us in no doubt about the importance of Quality Assurance and the undoubted pressure to provide better and safer quality systems.

## Supplier Evaluation

### Introduction

A major determinant of quality is the quality of supplies. This refers to anything supplied to the company whether it be material or services. There is sometimes confusion over terminology which needs to be resolved. For example, whenever ISO 9001 refers to the supplier it means the organisation seeking certification. Their suppliers are referred to as sub-contractors. Another term used for sub-contractors is vendors. As far as this section is concerned, the terms supplier and subcontractor will mean the same thing, whether it be for materials or services. Another term often used in place of purchasing is procurement. This is commonly used in MOD contracts. Procurement is perhaps a more generic name since purchasing implies some payment, whereas procurement may not necessarily involve payment.

However, the important point is that the quality of sub-contracted product (remember product may include services), is under someone else's control and, therefore, presents a vulnerable situation as far as quality assurance is concerned. Organisations such as Marks and Spencer rely totally on their suppliers' quality assurance since they do not make anything themselves. Much can be learned from their methodologies.

### Methods of Controlling Suppliers

There is a wide range of approaches and techniques that can be adopted in controlling suppliers.

i.    Product/process specification

ii.   Trust

iii.  Sample evaluation

iv.   Receipt inspection

      (1)    100%

      (2)    Spot checking

      (3)    Percentage sampling

      (4)    Statistical sampling

v.        Second party assessment

        (1)      Initial evaluation visit

        (2)      Surveillance visits

        (3)      Systems audit

vi.       Buyer/seller partnership

vii.      Third party assessment.

A number of other factors need to be taken into account before deciding on the most appropriate supplier.

These include:

i.        Relative size of purchaser in relation to supplier

ii.       Risk or consequences if the supplied products are not suitable

iii.      Cost of control versus cost of defects.

## *Product/process specification*

In this approach, the product or process is detailed very precisely in a specification. For example, the specification for the printing of cheque books comprises some 50 pages along with templates for checking. All product and/or process parameters are clearly defined in such a way that if they are closely adhered to the product will conform to specification. This is an approach commonly used by Marks and Spencer. When issued to several sub-contractors, the final products will be indistinguishable from each other regardless of where they are made. Product Specifications can also be used as a basis for contract and auditing.

While there is less excuse for the sub-contractor getting it wrong there is no guarantee that he will always get it right. The sub-contractor would still have to have some means of controlling quality.

## *Trust*

Placing orders on trust means that no checks or other controls are considered necessary. The justification for this approach may be that:

i.     It is believed that the sub-contractor has all the necessary arrangements in place to prevent defects.

ii.    The consequences of finding something wrong after purchase is not serious or costly.

iii.   The purchaser considers that the subcontractor knows more about the product and its fitness for use than they do.

This is a very common approach. Even when purchasers have strict inspection or other controls in place, it is likely that the scope of inspection or controls is restricted to selected features with the remaining features being left to trust. Consider, for example, the purchase of a car. The buyer may go over it with a fine toothcomb checking for obvious damage, together with a test drive prior to acceptance. However, it is highly unlikely that they will inspect anything that is not easily accessible, such as brake pads, for compliance to specification.

The basis of trust may have various foundations:

a.     naive or blind faith

b.     reputation

c.     recommendation

d.     past experience

e.     third party certification.

## *Sample evaluation*

Prior to placing orders for large quantities, the purchaser may require some evidence that what is to be supplied complies with his requirements. It is not uncommon, therefore, especially with large volume production to require the sub-contractor to supply samples which can be evaluated. This approach is usually employed in conjunction with other approaches.

# Supplier Evaluation

## Receipt inspection

*100% inspection.*

This requires some clarification. 100% inspection may mean inspection of all attributes of a product, or all products, or both. It is rare to find that it is necessary to inspect all attributes of a product. Some parameters are more significant than others. Some parameters are not readily inspected or can only be inspected by a destructive test. Inspection may introduce its own errors. For example, if it is necessary to dismantle something to inspect it, something may be left out on re-assembly.

Although it may be considered important to perform a dimensional or functional inspection, or test at the goods receiving stage, the decision to carry out a formal Goods Received Inspection (GRI) requires careful consideration. For example, take a typical company and say they receive 1000 different batches per month, containing an average of 1000 components, each component may have approximately 20 different features that could be checked. If all components were to be checked, then the number of checks would be:

1000 different batches per month x 1000 components per batch x 20 features per component = 20,000,000 features to be checked per month

*(This would obviously require a considerable inspection resource)*

As a result of the number of checks involved, the organisation may decide:

i.   Not to check every batch or type, but who decides which batch to check - the inspector?

ii.  Not to check 100%, i.e. every component. This can be reduced by sampling (BS 6001) but there are a number of risks with sampling.

iii. Not to check all the different features on an item - only the key features but again who decides what a key feature is - the inspector?

Now, if the above gives a 1000% reduction giving 20,000 features per month to be checked, even checking one at a minute each feature will still take approximately two full time inspectors. Is it any wonder that organisations are often complaining that Goods Received Inspection is not cost effective and does not stop poor quality entering the factory?

# Introduction to Quality

Another important fact is that 100% inspection does not necessarily mean 100% detection. By way of an example, inspect every letter in the following extract and count the number of times the letter 'e' occurs. Note you may only look at it once. Do not go back or recount. That would be more than 100% inspection.

Another important fact is that 100% inspection does not necessarily mean 100% detection. By way of an example, inspect every letter in the following extract and count the number of times the letter 'e' occurs. Note you may only look at it once. Do not go back or recount. That would be more than one hundred percent inspection.

How many did you find? Ask a friend to do the same and compare your results. How can we be sure? 100% inspection is often no better than 90% reliable i.e. it often only detects 90% of the errors. On the other hand some parameters are so critical that they must be independently inspected several times before acceptance. A case in point is the seven-fold checking of every printed banknote prior to release.

How many did you find? Ask a friend to do the same and compare your results. How can confidence be placed in the results? 100% inspection is often no better than 90% reliable, i.e. it often only detects 90% of the errors. On the other hand some parameters are so critical that they must be independently inspected several times before acceptance. A case in point is the seven-fold checking of every printed banknote prior to release.

*Spot checks*

This approach may be suitable for sub-contractors of known reliability. The checks are usually random and arbitrary. It is based on the same foundation of trust as above.

*Percentage sampling*

This is a very common approach to inspection usually based on 10% inspection regardless of the batch size. However, it is not commonly known that the approach is fundamentally flawed. A 10% sample of a batch of 5000 items means inspecting 500 items. While 10% of a batch of 50 items means inspecting only five items. The former is a much more stringent test and provides much less risk of accepting a defective batch than the latter. Hence this approach is only consistent with fixed batch sizes. See section Operating Characteristic Curves.

# Supplier Evaluation

## Second Party Evaluation

The previous section presented a defensive approach towards the control of supplies. Many companies, particularly those with a strong purchasing power, prefer to employ a preventive approach. Second party evaluation means that the purchaser carries out an evaluation of the subcontractor's ability to meet the purchaser's quality standards.

Second party evaluation may be done in varying degrees on a scale as follows:

i.      At a distance by monitoring delivery records and grading subcontractors on some scale.

ii.     By the use of questionnaires to solicit information about the company to enable some evaluation to be made. This is useful for carrying out comparisons between alternative subcontractors.

iii.    By visiting the subcontractor's premises to see for themselves how quality is controlled.

iv.     By assessing the subcontractor against some standard. This was the basis of the Ministry of Defence Approved Contractors List (ACL).

v.      By the location of a Quality Assurance Representative at the subcontractor's premises to continuously monitor that contractual requirements, including the quality management systems, are being complied with.

vi.     By regular surveillance visits to verify that quality systems are being maintained.

Surveillance visits vary from full systems audits to simple verification that systems are being maintained by examination of the quality system and/or inspection records.

## *Buyer/Seller partnerships*

More and more corporations are now treating their subcontractors as partners in their bid to retain the competitive edge through quality and reliability.

The larger corporations such as Ford Motor Company strike a deal with their subcontractors that they will continue to buy from them on condition that they enter into a continuous improvement programme. The buyers in this case agree to provide training and development programmes to enable the subcontractor to improve their systems and introduce modern TQM methodologies. Ford Motor Company has been doing this for some time now. Techniques that Ford require subcontractors to implement include Quality Function Deployment, FMECA's, Quality Planning and Statistical Process Control. Japanese companies go further and require the implementation of Quality Circles, Kaizen Quality Improvement Teams and the 5-S's. (See below for a summary of these tools and techniques).

During their surveillance visits the buyers check that there is evidence of these activities being actively applied to all their products or processes.

## *Third party certification*

The major problem with second party evaluation is the prospect of multiple assessment. That is, if a subcontractor has more than one major customer he may be subjected to second party surveillance by each of them. This is not only time consuming but may also create conflicting demands.

It was for this very reason that the British Standards Institute in 1979 published BS 5750 which was later to be adopted by the ISO committee as ISO 9000. In conjunction with this standard, more than 60 certification bodies have been formed and accredited to provide a certificate of assessment to those firms that can demonstrate that they meet the requirements of the standard. Thus by having one certification body the number of visits is restricted to two a year on average. At the same time, purchasers can be assured that subcontractors listed in the DTI (Department of Trade and Industry) register of firms of Assessed Capability are managing quality in accordance with an international standard.

This scheme is described in greater detail in an earlier unit.

## *QS 9000*

The car industry has been reluctant to give up their second party involvement with subcontractors. In addition, they considered that the ISO standard did not adequately address the controls considered essential in the manufacture of automotive parts. As a result they have collectively compiled an automotive industry version of ISO 9000 called QS 9000. In addition to the basic requirements of ISO 9000, QS 9000 includes various tools and techniques appropriate to the design and manufacture of automobiles.

## Supplier Evaluation

Thus, Supplier Assurance ranges from the fairly basic approach as described in ISO 9001 (see section on Purchasing) to the very comprehensive approaches, such as the Motor Vehicle Standard QS 9000. Both of these approaches have features that make the approach attractive to buyers; the simple approach may be less demanding in terms of resource but may be considered too vague and not sufficiently product or service specific.

### Elements for consideration when compiling a Purchasing Control procedure

Purchasing procedures should ensure that:

a) Requirements are clearly specified

b) Supplier performance is known

c) Any specific quality requirements are specified.

### a) The purchase order:

The Purchase Order should contain all the necessary information for the supplier to satisfactorily fulfil the customer requirements.

The order could contain:

○ Name and address of subcontractor from Approved List of Subcontractors

○ Identification, description and technical (drawing specification, etc.) information

○ Any Inspection and Test criteria (including certification) or Quality Standards to be applied

○ Delivery instructions

○ Review of the order (checking and approval of the above).

### b) Assessment of subcontractors:

This could include an audit against the requirements of a recognised Quality Assurance System Standard like ISO 9001 and assessing their ability to meet the customer requirements.

# Introduction to Quality

The creation of an Approved List of Subcontractors is usually an internally created list produced as a result of:

o   Vendor Rating or from commercially available lists of companies of assessed capability provided by certification bodies or the Department of Trade & Industry

o   Sending questionnaires to existing or prospective subcontractors requesting information about the supplier's Quality Assurance Management System

o   Examination of the supplier's historical performance by the use of such techniques as Vendor Rating.

*Vendor Rating:* Views on supplier's performance can be very subjective when making a decision on the selection of a subcontractor. As far as possible, supplier performance should be based on objective evidence by one or more of the methods described above. Often, subcontractors are selected on the basis of one person's judgement of a particular supplier's performance. This judgement may be on the basis of price alone. Price alone is not a good basis on which to place an order. Many organisations would be willing, and do pay a price premium for supplies that are to the correct quality and delivered on time. In fact, studies have shown that the customer is willing to pay a price premium of up to 30% if the perceived quality standard is higher than the competitors.

There are a number of other factors which may be considered other than price. Although price does need to be included when making a judgement on suppliers' performance. These factors can include:

Price   The rating needs to include price as a factor but because there are various types of subcontractor, e.g. subcontractors of apples and subcontractors of pears, comparing the price of apples with the price of pears is not appropriate. Also, the items are often obtained from a single source so comparing different subcontractors on the basis of price becomes difficult. One way of overcoming the problem of comparing subcontractors, e.g. subcontractor A's apples with subcontractor B's apples, can be to monitor price increases from the original order price with subsequent orders.

On Time Delivery  Number of deliveries on time against the number of late deliveries.

Quality          i)  Number of batches rejected against the number of orders accepted.

(This can include any subsequent problems with deliveries found later).

ii) Results of any external assessment by giving the subcontractor a rating on a scale from 0 (poor) to 10 (excellent).

Service          Subjective judgement on the subcontractor's ability to react to problems (quality, schedule changes, technical support etc.).  This may require discussion with buyers and engineers to determine the quality of service provided using a rating scale of 0 (poor) to 10 (excellent).

Each of these factors can be given a weighting, for example:

Price            30%

Delivery         20%

Quality          30% (if no audit rating figure)

15% for rejects + 15% for external audit rating. (The audit rating is a numerical interpretation of the results of an external audit)

Service          20%

*Note: These weightings are not fixed and may be modified for different situations.*

The following is an illustration of the way a Vendor Rating Analysis may be carried out to compare two potential suppliers.

**Table 7** An Example of Vendor Rating Analysis

| Factor | Weighting | Formula | Sub-contractor A | Sub-contractor B |
|--------|-----------|---------|------------------|------------------|
| Price | 30% | Original Price * 30% | 10 * 30%=25 | 12 * 30%=24 |
| | | Current Price | 12 | 15 |
| Delivery | 20% | On time delivery  * 20% | 54 * 20%=18 | 50 * 20%=20 |
| | | Total no. of Deliveries | 60 | 50 |
| Quality | 30% | No. of batch accepted * 15% | 32 * 15 | 45 * 30=27 |
| | | Total no. of batches | 60 | 50 |
| | | + | + | |
| | | Audit Rating * 15% | 6 * 15   =17 | (No audit) |
| | | | 10 | |
| Service | 20% | Service Rating * 20% | 5 * 20=10 | 9 * 20=18 |
| | | | 10 | 10 |
| Rating | 100% | | 70 | 89 |

It is important to remember to keep the analysis relatively simple as the Vendor Rating is only a guide to the supplier's performance and does not replace communication, discussion and generally working with the sub-contractor towards the common objective of improving the overall quality performance.

**c)      Goods Receiving Inspection (GRI):**

Almost all organisations perform some form of GRI. It may take the form of a complete inspection and test of the items received against a specification, possibly employing a sampling scheme such as BS 6001. Alternatively, GRI may consist of a check only on quantity, documentation, identification and damage.

## Sub-contractor Quality Assurance

### *Introduction*

The following approach towards second party assessment is based on the QS 9000 scheme.

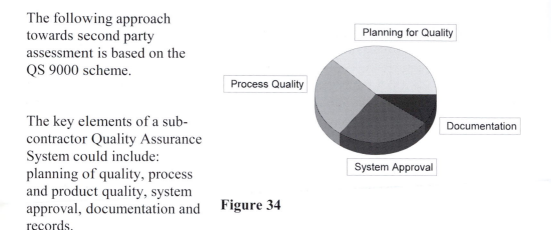

The key elements of a sub-contractor Quality Assurance System could include: planning of quality, process and product quality, system approval, documentation and records.

**Figure 34**

(See **Figure 34**)

### *a)        Planning for quality*

The following techniques can be employed to plan for quality, ensuring that before volume supplies or high cost installation is started, all possible sources of poor quality have been considered and addressed.

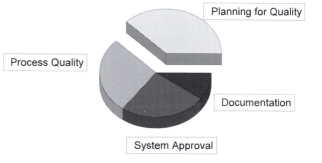

*Quality Function Deployment:*  As a project or design progresses, the greater

**Figure 35**

# Introduction to Quality

the chance that specific customer's needs and expectations are overlooked or not satisfied. In order not to neglect or overlook 'the voice of the customer', the Quality Function Deployment (QFD) technique has been developed. The aim of QFD is to identify the key customer needs and translate these needs into controls. This control is achieved by establishing what the customer requires and, through the various stages of QFD, how these requirements will be achieved.

*Failure Mode Effects and Criticality Analysis:* This technique is used to identify and eliminate possible causes of failure. The technique requires a sequential, disciplined approach by a team to assess systems, products or processes. The technique involves establishing the modes of failure and the effects of failure on the system, product or process. This ensures that all possible failure modes have been fully identified and ranked in order of their importance. (See section FMECA).

*Quality Control Planning:* Once the QFD and FMECA are completed an excellent understanding of the customer needs and expectations will have been gained. Any potential system or product failures will also have been identified. Consequently, the process or project can be properly planned.

The stages involved are:

i.    Defining the process. This can often be established by drawing a flow diagram of the process showing each of the key process stages and the sequence.

ii.   Identifying the parameters or key stages that require control.

iii.  Specifying the criteria for judging conformity

iv.   Deciding on the means of control

v.    Deciding on the means of assessment

vi.   Preparing the appropriate documentation

vii.  Monitoring the effectiveness of the plan.

*Process capability studies:* All processes are subject to variation. This variation may be small and insignificant or alternatively the variation could be excessive allowing products to be manufactured outside the specification. It is, therefore, important to understand the extent to which a process will vary before starting manufacture, thereby avoiding costly scrap or start/stop manufacture.

## Supplier Evaluation

One method of determining the ability of a process to meet specification is by conducting a Process Capability Study. This is where the process is statistically evaluated to determine the process ability to conform to specification.

### *b)* *Process and product quality*

*Statistical Quality Control (SQC):* Having determined the ability of the process to meet specification, controls need to be applied which continually monitor the process for quality and make continuous improvements. This involves taking regular measurements of process variation and comparing these observations with pre-determined control limits of

**Figure 36**

variation. This comparison can best be accomplished graphically on control charts. The application of SQC gives the opportunity to implement operator quality control, assisting in reinforcing the operator's responsibility for the quality of his own work and gives a sense of pride in his work.

### *c)* *System and product approval*

*Assessment, review and evaluation:* When a product specific Quality Control Plan has been established, then an audit can be performed to confirm compliance with the agreed Quality Plan including the application of SQC. The results of the assessment can then be reviewed and evaluated to identify any areas for possible improvement.

**Figure 37**

## Introduction to Quality

*Initial sample approval:* Provide statistical data in the form of Process Capability Study results to confirm the ability to manufacture all product features to the specified requirements.

### d)      *Documentation and records*

*Procedures:* When the above stages have been completed, then procedures need to be documented that describe the tasks to be performed together with any specific work instructions that may be necessary. These procedures may be subject to change. In the event of changes being necessary, change control procedures need to be agreed to ensure that documentation

**Figure 38**

is circulated to the relevant departments and that the documentation is kept up-to-date.

*Records:* Various records will need to be maintained providing documentary evidence of the satisfactory completion of the above stages, e.g. QFD and FMECA. Records of the inspection and testing performed will also need to be maintained, possibly in the form of SQC or Process Capability Study results.

# Part 4

# Quality Costs

# Quality Costs

## Introduction

The Quality Department is often considered to be another cost burden on the company and not one that could make a positive contribution towards the company profitability. Nothing could be further from the truth and the quality function is capable of making essential contributions towards the financial performance of the company. Not only

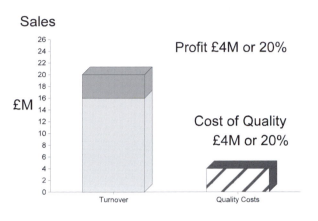

**Figure 39** Typical Cost of Quality

from the point of view of making a quality product that would consequently secure a strong position in the marketplace, but also by making significant savings in the overheads of the company.

**Justification** (Stage 1 - Sell)

It is essential to convince management of the need to investigate the cost of quality in order to gain their commitment and active participation in the cost of quality programme. The method of convincing management could be based on the following.

Consider a company with sales of £20M and making profits of 20%. Investigations in to the cost of quality at a number of companies have shown that the cost of quality will typically lie between 5% and 25% of the company's turnover. (See **Figure 39**).

# Quality Costs

Now, if a 50% improvement in profits is targeted, i.e. £6M. To achieve this new target then one approach could be to improve sales by a similar amount, i.e. 50% providing the increased profit of £2M. (See **Figure 40**).

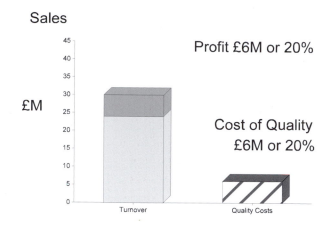

**Figure 40** Sales Improved by 50%

Using this approach to achieve the targeted £6M profit will involve a large financial investment together with a major expansion programme, obviously involving considerable risks, particularly if it is set against a background of fierce market competition.

There is, however, another approach, that is to reduce the cost of quality by 50%. This will produce the same effect, saving £2M and meeting the target figure of £6M. (See **Figure 41**). Now it is worth considering which is easier to achieve, a further 50% market penetration or to reduce the cost of quality by 50%. Which of these

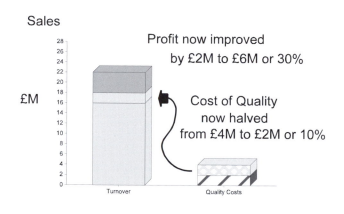

**Figure 41** 50% Reduction in the Cost of Quality

two exercises would require the greater resource to accomplish? The answer would largely depend on the industry involved, but this exercise does give an indication of the saving that can be made without resorting to a major expansion programme with all its inherent risks. In fact there are no risks involved in trying to reduce quality costs other than committing resources to achieve the objective. So, the Quality

138

# Introduction to Quality

Department can have a major impact on the profitability and performance of the company. The concept that is being suggested is that going for the avoidable quality costs can have major benefits without major risks. How do we undertake an attack on the avoidable quality costs?

There are a number of different approaches that can be adopted to establish and reduce the cost of quality. For example, a company or organisation-wide approach, which involves identifying and detailing the total cost of quality for the organisation. This is the Prevention, Appraisal, Failure Cost Model or PAF Model. Alternatively an individual department, process or task approach could be adopted, where the process is analysed with the objective to identify the conformance and non-conformance costs and to eliminate or reduce the non-conformance costs. This is known as the Process Cost Model (see page 152). This Process Costs Model approach can be used on a departmental basis or in organisations where the more traditional Prevention, Appraisal, Failure cost model does not appear to work. Another approach may be to evaluate the relationship between profits and costs of an organisation. To determine a way in which these two factors can be altered to best effect, see Profit/Cost Model. The first approach described is the overall company wide approach - the PAF Model.

# Quality Costs

## Prevention, Appraisal and Failure Model (PAF Model)

**Table 7** describes a quality cost reduction programme associated with the PAF Model.

Cost of Quality Reduction Programme

**Table 7**

| Stages in a Quality Cost Programme | | |
|---|---|---|
| Stage | Name | Description |
| 1 | Sell | To establish whether it is viable to examine the cost of quality. Then to justify a programme to higher management to gain their commitment and agreement to provide allocation of resources. |
| 2 | Information | To find the key categories that go to make up the total quality cost. |
| 3 | Measurement | To assess the cost of each individual category and to decide how frequently the information should be gathered, together with establishing what resources should be allocated to gathering the data. |
| 4 | Analysis | To decide how the data will be analysed and when the results will be published and what form the results will take. |
| 5 | Action | To produce a programme that will affect a reduction in quality costs. Also to establish how this programme will be implemented and introduced including dates and targets. |

# Introduction to Quality

**Quality Cost Categories:** (Stage 2 - Information)

What are the major factors that go to make up the total cost of quality?  Well, basically there are four, **Table 8** below explains each of the factors.

**Table 8** Cost of Quality - definition

| Quality Cost Categories | |
|---|---|
| Prevention Cost | The cost of action taken to examine, avoid or reduce the number of defects and failures. |
| Appraisal Cost | The cost of assessing the achieved quality standard. |
| *Failure Cost: The cost arising as a result of failing to achieve the required quality standard, which can be broken down into internal and external failure.* | |
| Internal Failure Cost | Internal failure being within the organisation (e.g. scrap). |
| External Failure Cost | External failure being outside the organisation (e.g. warranty claims).  This cost has often been found to be by far the largest expenditure and can be as high as 90% of the cost of quality. |

The proportion shown in **Figure 42** typically reflects the expenditure or losses incurred against each category. The largest cost of quality is usually found to be failure costs, particularly warranty costs. The smallest cost

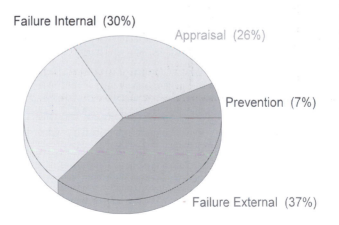
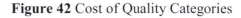

**Figure 42** Cost of Quality Categories

141

of quality is usually prevention cost, the money spent on avoiding poor quality.

The traditional approach to reducing the cost of quality was to attack the failure costs by increasing the appraisal costs (i.e. sorting the quality in). This would give the desired effect of stopping the customer receiving poor quality but has the knock on effect of increasing the internal failure costs (i.e. more scrap) and an increase in the appraisal costs (i.e. more inspectors). In order to break this cycle it is necessary to take preventive measures to stop the poor quality being produced in the first place, i.e. right first time.

So if we examine the cost of quality on the basis of prevention, appraisal and failure costs then this would assist in understanding the financial balance between these three factors. This information could be used in making judgements as to what the expenditure should be on prevention, appraisal and failure and to implement a cost reduction programme.

A typical company's cost of quality has been compiled. The break down of the costs can be seen in a spread sheet table. This table also shows some of the factors which are likely to make a contribution to the overall costs (see **Table 9**).

**Data Collection** (Stage 3 - Measurement)

The cost of each of these categories now needs to be established (see **Table 9**). To accomplish this task it is often wise to elicit the assistance of the company accountant to review the list of categories and to advise, and in certain cases, obtain the required data.

Some data may not be readily available and some means of data collection could become necessary or in certain circumstances accurate estimating may be appropriate, such as in establishing the cost of any quality planning carried out by the design department. (See Control of Non-Conforming Product and Corrective Action).

Some of the data could be already available but not in a suitable format, e.g.

o       Staff and hourly paid payroll

o       Scrap reports

o       Rework reports

o       Customer returns and field service data etc.

o       Transport costs

o       Design change notes.


*The pound rule:* It is worth spending a little time examining the cost of change as this can constitute a considerable amount of the cost of quality. If the cost of change is examined at each stage in a project then it can be seen that after each stage the cost of change will increase. (See **Figure 43**) For example:

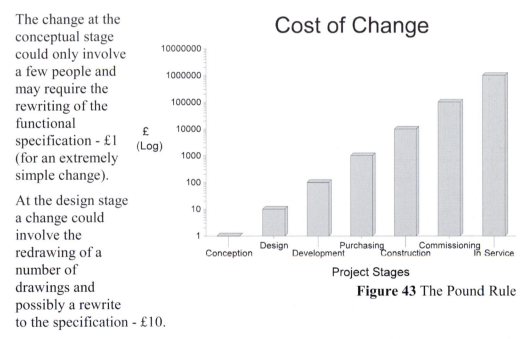

The change at the conceptual stage could only involve a few people and may require the rewriting of the functional specification - £1 (for an extremely simple change).

At the design stage a change could involve the redrawing of a number of drawings and possibly a rewrite to the specification - £10.

**Figure 43** The Pound Rule

A change at the development stage could involve redrawing and further trials and tests - £100.

If the change occurs at the purchasing of equipment and material stage, this could involve extensive discussion with the supplier, changes to purchase orders and specification - £1000.

# Quality Costs

If construction or manufacturing has started and changes are required (possibly due to sub-assemblies not working or fitting together) then it can start to become extremely expensive, it may involve redesign and retesting of the new configuration - £10000.

At the commissioning stage changes may be required due to the product not passing the tests and trials. Man weeks of work may be required to resolve the problem of making the product work satisfactorily and to customer requirements. A large investment has been made which cannot be recouped as the customer will not pay until the product works properly. In the worse case there may be penalty clauses for late delivery - £100,000.

In service and under warranty, if the product requires recall or a campaign change then the costs can be dramatic to the extent that companies become insolvent because of these excessive costs. Possibly the classic case of the cost of change is the Shuttle Challenger - £1,000,000.


*The pound rule* indicates that a pound invested at the start of a project could provide savings by a factor of 10 for each subsequent stage of the project. Note, it may be considered that some of the estimated costs of change are very conservative.

**Table 9** Spread Sheet showing the Cost of Quality

| Cat No. | Cost Category | Jan/Mar | Apr/Jun | Jul/Sep | Oct/Dec | Total £K | Target £K | Diff £K |
|---|---|---|---|---|---|---|---|---|
| | Company: QM&T | Location | GUILDFORD | | Year: | 1994/5 | | |
| | | | Quarters | | | | | |
| | **PREVENTION COSTS** | | | | | | | |
| P1 | Quality Mg't & Sup'n | 5031 | 5011 | 5039 | 5546 | 20.6 | 25 | 4.3 |
| P2 | Quality Engineering | 4258 | 4227 | 3935 | 3988 | 16.4 | 16 | -0.4 |
| P3 | Reliability Assessment | 93 | 6 | 77 | 163 | 0.3 | 3 | 2.6 |
| P4 | Audit | 500 | 500 | 500 | 500 | 2.0 | 2 | 0 |
| P5 | Supplier Assessment | 636 | 590 | 424 | 16 | 1.7 | 3 | 1.3 |
| P6 | Quality Training | 437 | 265 | 250 | 586 | 1.5 | 5 | 3.5 |
| P7 | Calibration | 399 | 325 | 425 | 376 | 1.5 | 4 | 2.5 |
| P8 | Equip't (Engineering) | 990 | 288 | 515 | 1217 | 3.0 | 3 | 0 |
| | Total Prevention Costs | 12344 | 11212 | 11165 | 12392 | 47.0 | 61 | 14 |
| | **APPRAISAL COSTS** | | | | | | | |
| A1 | Laboratory Test'g | 48 | 52 | 16 | 463 | 0.6 | 1000 | 0.4 |
| A2 | In-Process Inspection | 39336 | 39714 | 39201 | 39201 | 15.7 | 150 | -7.4 |
| A3 | Insp'n & Test Equip't | 2008 | 1916 | 776 | 402 | 0.5 | 12 | 6.9 |
| A4 | Goods Rec'g Inspect'n | 4623 | 4590 | 4540 | 4548 | 18.3 | 20 | 1.7 |
| A5 | Product Quality Audit | 609 | 600 | 636 | 636 | 2.4 | 3 | 0.5 |
| | Total Appraisal Costs | 46624 | 46872 | 45169 | 45250 | 2,126 | 1095 | 2.1 |
| | **INTERNAL FAILURE** | | | | | | | |
| I1 | Scrap | 33981 | 31947 | 22515 | 25533 | 11.4 | 100 | -14 |
| I2 | Rectification & Rework | 14274 | 13056 | 12420 | 16695 | 56.4 | 50 | -6.4 |
| I3 | Cost of Change | 3636 | 429 | 183 | 69 | 4.3 | 0 | -4.3 |
| I4 | Concessions | 1530 | 348 | 135 | 42 | 20.5 | 0 | -2.1 |
| | Total Internal Failure | 53421 | 45780 | 35253 | 42339 | 92.6 | 150 | -26.8 |
| | **EXTERNAL FAILURE** | | | | | | | |
| E1 | Warranty Returns | 31076 | 34471 | 34805 | 33212 | 133.6 | 100 | -33.5 |
| E2 | Complaints | 3732 | 3258 | 3066 | 3318 | 13.4 | 15 | 1.6 |
| E3 | Product Liability | 15000 | 0 | 0 | 0 | 15.0 | 15 | 0 |
| E4 | Warranty Spares | 15040 | 15289 | 15746 | 15460 | 61.5 | 50 | -11.5 |
| | Total External Failure | 64848 | 53018 | 53617 | 51990 | 223.4 | 180 | -43.4 |
| | TOTAL COST OF QUALITY | 177237 | 156882 | 145204 | 151971 | 631.3 | 577 | -54.3 |
| | Sales Revenue | 1004104 | 1001515 | 1002477 | 1001791 | 4009 | 3600 | -410 |
| | Manufacturing Costs | 802575 | 810433 | 836565 | 835620 | 3285 | 4000 | 714.9 |
| | Direct Labour Cost | 195686 | 187006 | 186888 | 180452 | 750 | 1200 | 450 |
| | % Cost of Quality/Sales | 17.7% | 15.7% | 14.5% | 15.2% | 15.7% | 16.0% | |
| | % Scrap Cost/Manufactur'g | 4.2% | 3.9% | 2.7% | 3.1% | 3.5% | 2.5% | |
| | % Rectifi'n/Direct Labour | 7.3% | 7.0% | 6.6% | 9.3% | 7.5% | 4.2% | |
| | % Warranty Spares/Sales | 1.5% | 1.5% | 1.6% | 1.5% | 1.5% | 1.4% | |

## Quality Costs

**Investigation** (Stage 4 - Analysis)

Having identified the cost of each of the categories then these costs need to be analysed as a prelude to taking action to reduce the total cost.  The analysis can be accomplished by various methods:

i)  Comparison between prevention, appraisal and failure costs.

This provides the first snapshot of the way by which quality is organised and gives an initial guide as to whether the right balance is being maintained

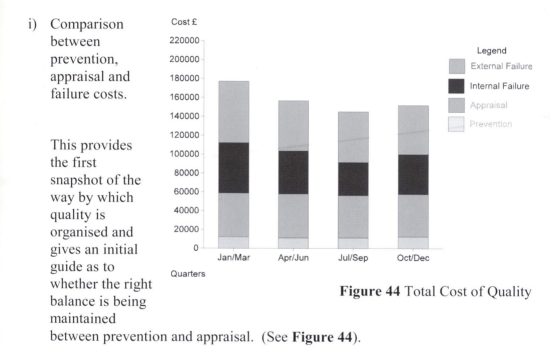

**Figure 44** Total Cost of Quality

between prevention and appraisal.  (See **Figure 44**).

ii)  Comparison by time.

Analysis of quality cost data on the basis of time is essential in indicating trends, monitoring performance and to ascertain whether real improvements are being made, reducing the cost of quality.

iii) Comparison between products or departments.

The cost data can also be arranged by product or department to enable comparisons to be made between the relative performance of one product with another, or one department with another.

iv) Bases

The cost figures by themselves indicate the expenditure on quality. However, to establish a true and consistent guide as to the relative costs, it is necessary to relate the costs to different bases or indices. Some examples of quality cost indices can be:

a)      Labour hours - Number of personnel involved in production or direct labour hours.

$$\% \ Rectification \ = \ \frac{Rectification \ Hours \ * \ 100\%}{Direct \ Labour \ Hours} \qquad \textbf{(1)}$$

The comparison of rectification hours is based on the time spent on rectifying bad products against the time spent on making good products. This comparison could be demonstrated graphically showing the year's percentage rectification performance.

$$\% \ Cost \ of \ Appraisal \ = \ \frac{Inspection \ Hours \ + \ Test \ Hours \ Hours \ * \ 100\%}{Direct \ Labour \ Hours} \textbf{(2)}$$

## Quality Costs

The cost of appraisal is a comparison of the time spent making the product against the time spent inspecting and testing the product.

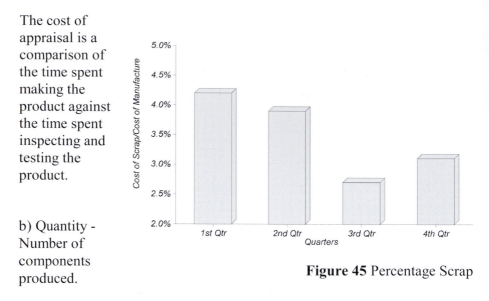

b) Quantity - Number of components produced.

**Figure 45** Percentage Scrap

The percentage scrap calculation compares the number of bad components made against the number of good components made. (Sometimes referred to as yield). See **Figure 45**.

$$\% \; Scrap \; = \; \frac{Number \; of \; Components \; Scrapped \; * \; 100\%}{Number \; of \; Components \; Produced} \qquad \textbf{(3)}$$

The calculation of percentage warranty compares the number of products returned faulty with the number of products sold and provides some indication of the changes in the proportion of warranty returns.

$$\% \; Warranty \; Returns \; = \; \frac{Number \; of \; Warranty \; Returns \; * \; 100\%}{Total \; Number \; of \; Products \; Sold} \qquad \textbf{(4)}$$

c) Costs

o        Value of the output (unaffected by the fluctuation in sales)

o        Manufacturing cost (Labour + material costs)

o        Value of the sales.

$$\% \ Total \ Cost \ of \ Quality \ = \ \frac{Total \ Cost \ of \ Quality \ * \ 100\%}{Value \ of \ the \ Output} \qquad (5)$$

The total cost of quality calculation compares the money spent on quality against the value of the output. **Figure 44**, Total Cost of Quality, shows the changes in the percentage total cost of quality throughout the year, together with the proportion of the costs spent on prevention, appraisal and failure. The diagram also shows the changes in the proportions of prevention, appraisal and failure.

## Optimum Quality

According to the PAF[14] model of the cost of quality model there is an economic limit to quality improvement. There comes a point where the cost of prevention is greater than the savings made by the reduction of defects. However, this is based on purely financial grounds and there may be other more important considerations such as risk to life.

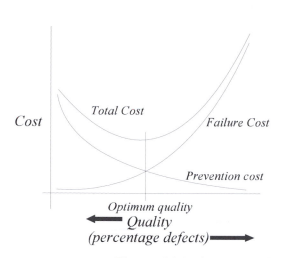

**Figure 46** Optimum Quality?

This graph of optimum quality suggests that there is a relationship between failure and appraisal costs and the amount of money spent on prevention. I.e. if more money is spent on prevention then the failure costs will automatically reduce. Similarly, if less money is spent on prevention and appraisal then the failure costs will increase. In fact the graph suggests there is a direct relationship between these two expenditures. The graph also implies that there is a point of balance, where more expenditure on prevention will at some point become counter productive. Spending more on prevention will reduce failure costs but the law of diminishing returns will eventually take place. Consequently, there is a point of balance called the minimum cost of quality (maybe a better term is the point of mediocrity). This point (minimum cost of quality) implies that there is no point in spending any more resource or money preventing poor quality, as we are already at the optimum point. This is the argument for doing nothing: we are already doing the best we can, there are no more improvements to be made (the point of mediocrity).

The opposite argument is that it is not necessary to keep spending more and more on prevention to get the same failure cost reduction. All that is necessary is by some means to remember or retain the gains made on preventing poor quality, possibly by

---

14      Prevention, Appraisal, Failure BS6143 Part 2

recording the improvement in a new procedure. The graph implies that to achieve zero defects, infinite amounts of money will have to be spent on prevention. When the reality is that resource and money spent wisely on prevention will continually provide a return on investment as long as the improvements are retained. This graph has held sway for far too long. It encourages compliancy and satisfaction with current performance, when what we actually need is to motivate for improvement. One Purchasing Manager used this graph to explain how good his department's performance was and consequently there was no value to do any work on improvement. He considered his department was at the minimum cost of quality. What arrogant nonsense, where he and his department were actually placed, was at the minimum point of mediocrity.

## Action (Stage 5)

**Pareto Analysis** Establishing the factors which together make up all the various causes of rejects, invariably means that a considerable number of problems are discovered. To tackle all these problems at one go would require enormous resources and in any case some of the problems may be trivial and not worth pursuing for the time being. A technique invaluable in singling out those problems which have the greatest influence on the total reject quantity is Pareto Analysis. Very often when this type of analysis is conducted, the results show that when placed in order of importance out of a given number of causes of non-conformance, only a small percentage, usually around 20%, account for 80% of the total non-conformance problem. For this reason the concept is often known as the 80 - 20 rule, (see section on Pareto Analysis).

**Cause and Effect Diagrams** The first stage in completing a cause and effect diagram is for the team to clearly define the problem. Having established the group's views on the most likely cause of the effect or problem, the team then needs to consider what, in their view, is the most likely cause or suspect. These suspects or causes can be ranked in order of most likely or most easy to eliminate from the investigations. Having prioritised the suspects an action plan or investigation plan can be completed and implemented. This plan would detail the suspect name, the method of evaluating the suspect's guilt and who is responsible for conducting the investigation. This stage would be repeated until the actual culprit was discovered - it may even be necessary for the team to reconstruct another cause and effect diagram to assist in identifying the culprit. (See section on Cause and Effect Diagrams). In certain cases the problem may be so complex that more sophisticated statistical techniques may need to be employed (Taguchi Techniques). One of the reasons for employing Taguchi may be that there is no single factor or guilty party which is causing the problem, but several factors interacting together.

**Process Quality Costs Model**

Stages in establishing and reducing the process quality costs are outlined in **Table 10**.

**Table 10** Process Quality Cost Programme

| Stages in a Process Quality Cost Programme | | |
|---|---|---|
| Stage | Name | Description |
| 1 | Sell | To establish whether it is viable to examine the cost of quality. Then to justify a programme to higher management to gain their commitment and agreement to provide allocation of resources. |
| 2 | The Process | To identify the process to be analysed. Break the process down into discrete steps and tasks. |
| 3 | Process Analysis | To identify the inputs and outputs to the process. How the process is to be controlled and what resources are necessary for the process to work. |
| 4 | Process Quality Cost Reduction | To identify the costs associated with the process in terms of conformance and non-conformance costs and improve the process performance by the elimination of waste. |

**Justification**     (Stage 1 - Sell) (See Justification on Page 137)

This stage is the most important as without Management Commitment the Process Quality Cost programme cannot succeed.

**Process Selection**      (Stage 2 - The Process)

The process to be analysed needs to be identified. Once the process has been identified then it can be broken down into each discrete task or step. Process flow charting is one way of describing the process, showing the sequence and sometimes feedback loops. During this stage, an analysis can be performed, assessing the need for each task and gaining agreement as to whether the sequence and tasks are correct.

**Input/Output Analysis** (Stage 3 - Process Analysis)

The inputs and outputs to the process need to be identified, how the process is controlled and what resources are necessary. This analysis can either be done by constructing a simple description of the inputs to the process, the activities associated with the process and the outputs from the process.

*Process:* All the activities or tasks necessary to convert the process inputs into the process outputs.

*Inputs:* The inputs to the process are all the materiel (material, equipment, data etc.) necessary, for the process to convert successfully into the output.

*Output*: The results of the process conversion. All the material, data etc. that the process generates.

Due to the complexity of some processes it is a good idea to restrict the analysis to a single process, e.g. only material flow, paper work, information etc.

# Quality Costs

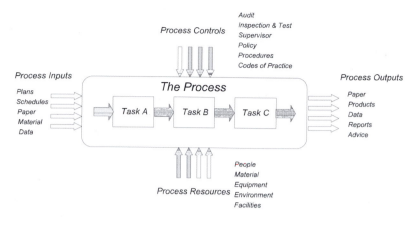

**Figure 47** Process Input/Output

Alternatively (see **Figure 47**) the analysis can be quite complex, not only detailing the inputs, activities and outputs but also the method of controlling the process (feedback mechanisms etc.) and the resources necessary for the process to take place.

*Process controls:* The method of controlling the process. How is the process controlled? Inspection & test activities, supervision monitoring, audits, feedback of results etc.

*Process resources:* The items or people that facilitate the conversion process. Not the items that are converted but those items which make the conversion process possible, e.g. people, equipment, data, information, facilities etc.

From this analysis it is possible to show how each of the tasks are linked together, the sequence and interdependence of the tasks. The diagram shown in **Figure 47** can then be analysed to ensure that:

- o    All the inputs must be available

- o    Each task must have an owner. (See Departmental Purpose Analysis)

- o    All of the tasks must be of value. (See Non-Value Added Activities)

- o    All of the outputs must go somewhere (if the outputs go nowhere, then they are unnecessary and should be deleted).

Due to the complexity of some processes it is sometimes a good idea to restrict the analysis to a single process, e.g. material flow, paper work, information etc.

Some other techniques that can be usefully employed in understanding and analysing the process are Failure Mode and Effects Analysis (FMEA) and Quality Planning. FMEA can help to identify the failure modes of the process and force some decision regarding the action to take to eliminate any potential failures of the process. For example the failure mode could be misunderstanding of the customers' requirements or needs. The action may be to get the customers to write down their requirements. If the possible failure mode cannot be eliminated then action needs to be taken to avoid the likelihood of the failure modes occurring; in this case Quality Planning can be helpful as it forces a description of the quality controls that will be applied at each stage to ensure process conformity. Again, the example of misunderstanding the customer needs - the customer it may not be capable or adequately skilled to define or write down their needs or requirements (often the customer does not know what they want!). In this case, Quality Planning may provide an approach, such as reviewing internally, with the key project personnel, the internally produced customer requirements.

**Action** (Stage 4 - Process Quality Cost Reduction)

Once the process is fully understood, it is then possible to evaluate the process to determine the necessary and unnecessary costs.

Completing a Failure Mode and Effects Analysis for the processes under investigation (see section Failure Mode and Effects Analysis) may help in determining the necessary and unnecessary costs. This is because part of the FMEA process is to identify possible and actual failure modes and their causes.

*Necessary Costs:* (Price of Conformance) Those activities and tasks associated with completing and getting the process right.

*Unnecessary Costs:* (Price of Non-Conformance) Those activities as a result of getting the activity or task wrong (unnecessary costs - the task necessary as a result of failure).

**Table 11** Process Quality Costs - for the Purchasing Department

| Process Name: Purchasing | | | | | Process Owner: Buyer | | | Date: |
|---|---|---|---|---|---|---|---|---|
| # | Description | Necessary Tasks | Time (min) | £ | Unnecessary Tasks | Time (min) | % Occ. | £ |
| 1 | Receive Purchase Requisitions | Reviewing/accepting the Purchase Requisition and up dating the purchase ledger. | 2 | 0.3 | Rejected purchase requisitions. Dealing with queries regarding order processing. | 10 | 5% | 0.08 |
| 2 | Identify supplier | Searching appropriate databases for an adequate supplier. | 10 | 1.7 | Failing to identify a supplier or no unqualified acceptance of the terms and conditions. Reordering in the event of a change of requirements or wrong information. | 30 | 1% | 0.05 |
| 3 | Complete the Purchase Order | Completing the Purchase Order (including gaining approval). Updating the Purchase Ledger. | 5 | 0.8 | Inadequate or incorrect information on the purchase requisition. | 20 | 5% | 0.17 |
| 4 | Liaise with Suppliers | Liaison and building up a good working relationship with the supplier. | 5 | 0.8 | Inadequate or incorrect information sent to the supplier. Additions, omissions or changes to the order. Chasing the status of the purchase order. | 30 | 4% | 0.20 |
| 5 | Receive purchased material | Goods Receiving and Inspection & testing. | 15 | 2.5 | Late delivery, rejection, poor service, defects, shortages, reconciliation of any discrepancies etc. | 40 | 3% | 0.20 |
| | | Total | 37 | 6.1 | Total | 130 | | 0.70 |

**Table 11** shows a Process Cost Model for the purchasing process. The table consists of:

Column 1    The task number

Column 2    The task description

Column 3    The necessary tasks - those activities necessary to complete the tasks correctly

Column 4    The time to complete the necessary tasks

Column 5    The cost of completing the necessary tasks i.e. time to complete x the labour rate e.g. 6 min/60 (hours) x £10/hour = £1

Column 6    If any unnecessary task occurs, the time to complete the unnecessary tasks - those activities necessary as a result of a task being incorrectly performed

Column 7    The time to complete the unnecessary tasks

Column 8    The likelihood of an unnecessary task occurring e.g. the average number of orders with incorrect information is usually about five in a hundred orders or 5%

Column 9    The average cost of completing an unnecessary task, i.e. time to complete x the likelihood of occurrence x labour rate e.g. when there is an incorrect information on an order, it usually takes 20 minutes to resolve, but an incorrect order will only happen in about five in a hundred orders.  Therefore, the cost will be:

(Time to resolve) 20 min/60 (hours) x (Likelihood of happening) 5% x (labour Rate) £10/hour = £0.17

# Quality Costs

## Comparison of the Total Cost of Quality with Process Quality Cost

The advantage of the Total Cost of Quality (TCQ) over the Process Quality Cost (PQC) approach is that the cost of quality for the whole organisation will be established whereas only the cost of quality for particular processes will be determined with the PQC approach. This tends to suggest that the TCQ approach is the best, unfortunately this is not always the case. For certain organisations it is very difficult to use the TCQ model as it does not fit the way the organisation works. For example, a service organisation servicing and repairing equipment, or a construction company does not fit the traditional TCQ model. Determining the internal and external costs is very difficult. However, analysing each individual service or design process in turn can expose the true hidden costs of quality. With design organisations, project planning or design reviews are quality tasks or part of the normal design activities and therefore part of the design costs and not a quality cost at all.

It is important to note that this is not an "either/or" situation; employing both techniques can be successful, possibly using the PQC model first to obtain and establish the individual process quality cost data, then collating all the information into the organisation's overall TCQ model.

## Problems with Cost of Quality Analysis & Data Collection

There are certain issues that need to be considered when compiling the Cost of Quality Data. Namely, there is a considerable amount of effort associated with collection of the data which is wasted if the data is not used or acted on. The frequency of data collection can vary but often is between quarterly to yearly. Monthly is generally too frequent. It is important to gather the data to confirm that improvements and savings are being made. If the wrong data is gathered or false information is collected this can give a false picture of the Cost of Quality. Care needs to be taken with the targets set for Cost of Quality as over-confident figures and, conversely, over-cautious targets will create a falsely optimistic picture of the future for the company.

158

## Loss Function - Genichi Taguchi

When a designer determines a tolerance or specification, is the tolerance determined by sophisticated means of analysing the optimum value by careful evaluation, tests, trials and calculations on the proposed design solution?  Or, alternatively, does the designer make an estimate or judgement based upon the designer's experience and skill?  The truth is more probably the latter (an estimate) rather than the former (tests and trials).  The reason being the time, expense and effort involved in completing the various trials, tests and calculations to determine the tolerance.  Sometimes, possibly because of lack of trust between the designer and the producer, the designer may specify too tight a tolerance believing that the producer will produce outside tolerance anyway.

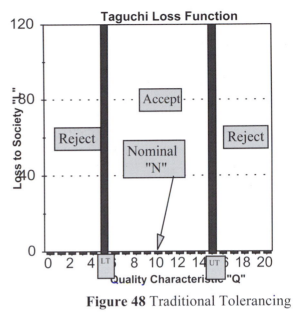

**Figure 48** Traditional Tolerancing

What does the manufacturing department do with these tolerances and how are the tolerances used?  Well, the tolerances will be used to determine whether a process should run or not and if the process output is acceptable.  As a consequence of this possibly arbitrary judgement by the designer, a considerable amount of money will be spent getting the process to run to tolerance and if rejects are produced that are judged to be outside tolerance these items may be scrapped. (See Statistical Tolerancing).  To the producer the tolerance is often seen as black and white.  **Figure 48** shows this situation.  Anything to the left of the LT (Lower Tolerance) line is a reject no matter how slightly to the left it is.  Anything to the right of the UT (Upper Tolerance) line is also a reject even though this may be only by an infinitely small amount.

## Quality Costs

Are tolerances black and white?  Well, Taguchi thinks not.  What must be aimed for is minimum variation (rather than some arbitrary tolerance) because minimum variation reduces losses to both the customer/society and the producer and improves quality.

Taking wire production as an example, the process capability of wire drawing is very good  (see section on Statistical Process Control).  Wire can be drawn or produced easily within the manufacturing tolerance.  One of the largest costs to a wire producer is the material (copper wire) used.  If the copper wire diameter is minimised (within the tolerance) then there are large material savings for the producer.  However, the consequence of minimising the diameter wire for the customer or society will be electrical power loss.  Minimisation of variation to an agreed nominal value will benefit both parties.

Often Quality Managers see their role as only ensuring the output meets the tolerance or specification, mistakenly thinking this alone will achieve customer satisfaction.  The tolerance is only one person's (designers) view on achieving the customer requirements and it may not be correct.  The Quality Manager blindly following the tolerance misses the point that it is the reduction in variation that will satisfy the customer.

Figure 49 shows how this minimisation of variation can affect the loss to society. Following the curved line, as the quality characteristic moves further away from the nominal or target value, the greater becomes the loss.

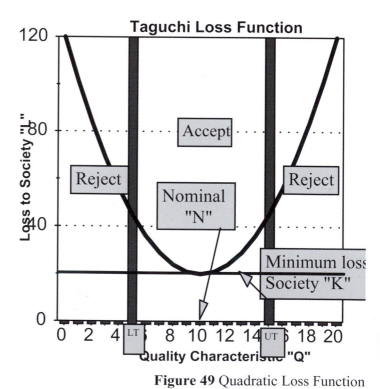

Figure 49 Quadratic Loss Function

160

# Introduction to Quality

The normal way of interpreting the tolerance is that any item inside the tolerance is acceptable. Any items below the lower tolerance and above the upper tolerance are rejected - black and white. In other words, if the Quality Characteristic is just slightly to the left of the Lower Tolerance or slightly to the right of the Upper Tolerance the items are rejected. However, if the Quality Characteristic is just slightly to the right of the Lower Tolerance or slightly to the left of the Upper Tolerance the items are accepted. Logically this is nonsense: how can a very small variation in the Quality Characteristic make an item acceptable or rejectable?

A better approach would be, if the variation in the quality characteristic around the nominal or target value was minimised, this would minimise the losses to both society and the company and improve the quality performance. This can be shown in the Taguchi Loss to Society equation and is represented in **Figure 49**.

$$Loss\ to\ Society\ L\ =\ C*(Q-N)^2 + K \qquad\qquad (6)$$

Where:

|     |     |
| --- | --- |
| N   | = Nominal |
| L   | = The loss to society |
| C   | = The cost coefficient |
| Q   | = The Quality Characteristic |
| K   | = A constant equating to the minimum loss to society |
| T   | = The tolerance |
| LT  | = The lower tolerance |
| UT  | = The upper tolerance |

The target must be therefore to minimise variation rather than just working to tolerance.

## Profit/Cost Model

Introduction

Whilst the PAF and PQC models are the more widely accepted methods of evaluating the costs of quality for organisations, there are other approaches which are just as effective, namely the profit/cost model.

The two previously described models tend to focus on identifying the areas where the failure or non-conformance costs are high and taking steps to reduce these costs. A different approach may be to evaluate the cost of production or delivering a service, with the aim of reducing the conformance costs, together with identifying ways in which to maximise the profitability of an organisation.

The relationship under investigation is the Profit/Cost ratio. The object being to improve the ratio by identifying the means of increasing profit and/or reducing costs.

$$Improving\ the\ Profit/Cost\ Ratio\ =\ \frac{Increasing\ the\ Profits}{Reducing\ the\ Costs} \qquad (7)$$

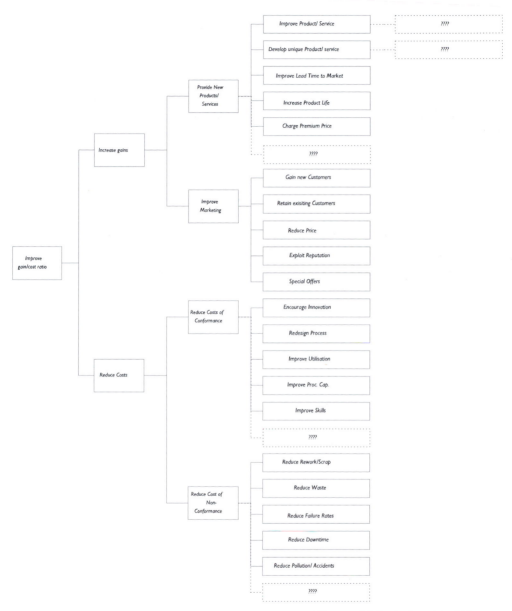

**Figure 50** Relationship Diagram

For non-profit making organisations, the profit aspect may be considered to be underspend on the organisation's budget without detrimentally affecting the quality of the delivered service or product.

Some more astute readers may have noticed a basic conflict with this ratio and TQM. *The primary purpose of a TQM organisation is not to make a profit but to satisfy the customer. Satisfying the customer will consequentially provide a profit!* Whether this statement is accurate or not, can be safely left to the TQM philosopher. Those from the school of - *if it works use it* - may still like to evaluate this approach.

## Guidelines

The method of conducting the analysis is initially the same as with the other Quality Cost models - *justification*. It is pointless to embark on a Quality Cost exercise without the active and visible support of the management team.

Next, the factors which affect profitability and costs need to be established. One of the methods that can be used is a relationship diagram shown in **Figure 50** (similar to a cause and effect diagram).

The left-hand side of the diagram shows the objective - improving the profit/costs ratio. To the right are the means of achieving this objective. Firstly increasing profit and reducing costs and so on. At the extreme right of the diagram are some question marks (????). This is deliberate to show how the diagram can be extended. For example, in the top box marked ???? could be - 'Better Guarantee' or 'Individualise the Product or Service'. Other ideas could be generated on how to improve the Product or Service branch of the diagram.

**Exercise - Cost of Quality**

The section Cost of Quality refers to three methods of determining the quality costs: the Prevention, Appraisal and Failure method (PAF Model), the Process Cost Model and the Profit/Cost model.

Using the above models, obtain sufficient data to apply each of these methodologies to an organisation and process of your choice.

1.      The output of the PAF methodology should be:

      i.      A Cost of Quality Spread Sheet

      ii.     Identification of the key cost of quality elements

      iii.    A brief action plan that would result in real reduction of the cost of quality for the organisation to which the exercise has been applied

2.      The output of the Process Cost Model should be:

      i.      A completed Process Quality Cost table (including both actual and synthetic costs)

      ii.     Identification of the key non-conformance costs

      iii.    A brief action plan which would result in real reduction of the cost of operating the process selected

3.      The output of the Profit/Cost Model should be:

      i.      A completed Profit/Cost Model relationship diagram

      ii.     A brief action plan that would result in real reduction of the cost of quality for the organisation to which the profit/cost model has been applied

# Part 5

# Statistical Process Control

**Statistical Process Control**

**Process Capability Studies**

**Process Variability**

No matter what precautions are taken, no two items are absolutely identical. Differences may be barely measurable but they exist and that is why tolerances are allowed on drawings and specifications.

A manufacturing process, no matter how precise, is subject to a very large number of random disturbances, each so small as to be individually insignificant, but which in combination cause the results of the process to deviate slightly from the objective.

The inherent variability thus caused is a characteristic of the process. It is the basic variability which is always present when that particular process is in operation and is called the RESIDUAL variability.

*The causes of variation can be divided into machine and process variations.*

**Machine variations**

Machine variations are purely and simply those variations attributable to the machine only. It is the best that a machine can be expected to produce given ideal conditions. Machines vary in their capabilities owing to their age and condition or the tolerances to which the machine was constructed. For a given machine some functions may be more capable than others. For example, a drilling machine will generally be more precise (have a better capability) on hole diameter than on position. Some examples of the relative capabilities of common manufacturing processes are shown below.

## *Typical Process Capabilities*

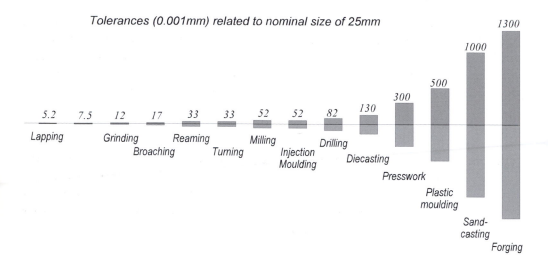

*Tolerances (0.001mm) related to nominal size of 25mm*

**Figure 51** Typical process capability

### *Process variations*

Process variations are those over and above the machine variations which are attributable to circumstances around the machine. They include the effect of environmental fluctuations such as temperature and humidity, variations in raw materials, variations in operator attention, variations from shift to shift and so on.

The first important check, therefore, is to consider whether the machine and subsequently the process are both capable of doing the job to the specification. This will require machine and process capability studies to be carried out.

# Introduction to Quality

The sources of variation can be further categorised into two types:

i)      Common causes, otherwise known as random causes

ii)     Special causes, otherwise known as non-random or assignable causes.


## i)      *Common causes*

Common causes appear to follow a random pattern and are due to inherent variations in the machine or process. For a particular machine or process, the pattern of variation will be characterised by its location, spread, and shape. The combination of these characteristics is called the machine capability in the case of the machine and the process capability in the case of the process. It is the natural tolerance of a stable machine or process.


In general, improvements in machine and process capabilities having only common cause variations, can only be achieved through detailed analysis to identify and isolate particular causes. This usually requires managerial action such as overhauling or replacing a machine, changing to more reliable supplies of materials, providing better tooling, providing further training for operators and so on.


## ii)     *Special causes*

Variations due to special causes do not form a random pattern but quite definitely indicate a shift, trend, cycle or otherwise systematic variation such as peaks or troughs. For a stable process, two thirds of the measurements should lie within the middle third of the capability band, with the other third being equally divided into the outer two thirds. In addition, no more than seven points in a row should be consistently above the mean, below the mean or progressively up or down.


In general, variations due to special causes can be controlled by local actions such as resetting the machine controls, taking a lighter cut, providing more immediate feedback of performance to the operator etc.

# Process Capability Studies

## *Process capability studies*

Before allocating a job to a given machine or process, it is necessary to establish whether the process is capable of meeting the specification. A simple approach is described below:

a)      Set the process to meet its target figure. This would normally be its mid point of specification.

b)      Ensure the process is stable and under control.

c)      Take 50 consecutive units from the process and measure them accurately to one more decimal place than the specified tolerance, e.g. if the specified tolerance is ±0.01mm, then measure to the nearest .001mm.

d)      Assuming that the distribution of results forms a smooth bell shaped curve (approximating a normal distribution - see section normal distribution), calculate the arithmetical mean $\overline{X}$ and the standard deviation $\sigma$ of the 50 units.

e)      The process capability (Cp) is considered to be six standard deviations ($6\sigma$). Now compare the six standard deviations with the specified tolerance thus:

$$Cp = \frac{specified\ tolerance}{6\sigma}$$

## *The potential process capability*

The potential process capability is the best that the process can achieve having eliminated special cause variations. The process is said to be stable when the variations are due to random causes only. Six standard deviations are considered to contain 99.7% of all items made. To determine if a process is capable the statistic Cp needs to be calculated. If Cp = 1 then approximately 3 in every 1,000 will be outside the specification. This means that values of Cp greater than 1, say 1.5 or even 2.0, are desirable. Diagrammatically this may look like this:

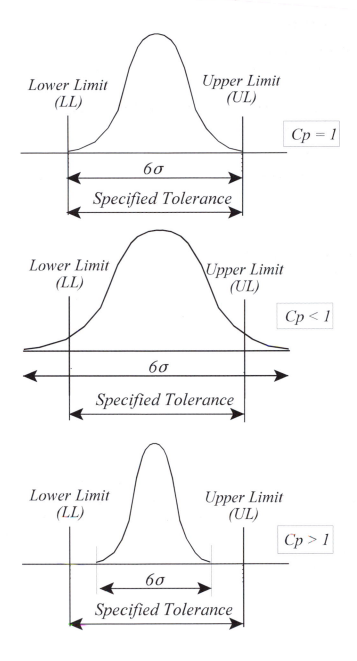

**Figure 52** Process capability

## Example

We are now going to work through an example based on the inspection results of a sample of 40 bolts. The following shows how raw data is turned into meaningful information. The diameter of a sample of 40 bolts was measured with the following results:

| | | | | | | | | | |
|------|------|------|------|------|------|------|------|------|------|
| 7.31 | 7.47 | 7.55 | 7.20 | 7.45 | 7.49 | 7.62 | 7.86 | 7.44 | 7.39 |
| 7.38 | 7.57 | 7.63 | 7.24 | 7.76 | 7.55 | 7.56 | 7.18 | 7.00 | 7.83 |
| 7.57 | 7.24 | 7.32 | 7.39 | 7.42 | 7.35 | 7.63 | 7.41 | 7.40 | 7.30 |
| 7.48 | 7.49 | 7.27 | 7.51 | 7.51 | 7.73 | 7.12 | 7.37 | 7.48 | 7.14 |

A chronological plot is produced to establish that there are no trends or patterns:

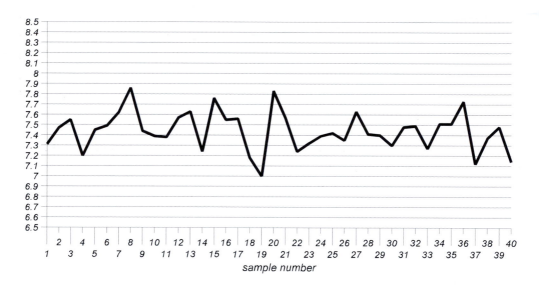

**Figure 53** Chronological plot of data

By drawing a frequency distribution we can confirm that it approximates to a normal distribution. The data must be grouped into approximately 10 intervals to create a frequency diagram. The boundaries of these intervals are called the *class limits*. The nominal value for each class interval is used to represent its respective class. A tally chart is used to record the number of items within each class.

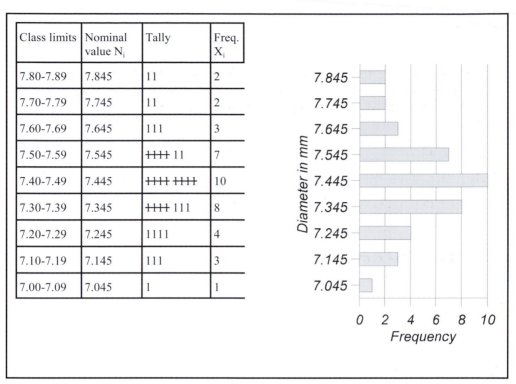

| Class limits | Nominal value $N_i$ | Tally | Freq. $X_i$ |
|---|---|---|---|
| 7.80-7.89 | 7.845 | 11 | 2 |
| 7.70-7.79 | 7.745 | 11 | 2 |
| 7.60-7.69 | 7.645 | 111 | 3 |
| 7.50-7.59 | 7.545 | ++++ 11 | 7 |
| 7.40-7.49 | 7.445 | ++++ ++++ | 10 |
| 7.30-7.39 | 7.345 | ++++ 111 | 8 |
| 7.20-7.29 | 7.245 | 1111 | 4 |
| 7.10-7.19 | 7.145 | 111 | 3 |
| 7.00-7.09 | 7.045 | 1 | 1 |

**Figure 54**

To determine the process capability we need to calculate the mean and hence the standard deviation of the raw data.

$$Mean \; \bar{x} = \frac{\sum_{i=1}^{i=40} x_i}{n}$$

$$\bar{x} = 7.440$$

$$Standard \; deviation \; \sigma = \sqrt{\frac{\sum_{i=1}^{i=40} \left(\bar{x} - x_i\right)^2}{n}}$$

$$\sigma = 0.1899$$

Process Capability $= 6\sigma = 1.139$

# Process Capability Studies

In other words, the process is currently producing components in the range:

$$\overline{x} \pm 3\sigma$$

$$= 6.8703 \text{ to } 8.0097$$

Now suppose that the specified tolerance was, say, $7.5 \pm 0.5$ then clearly, the process is not capable of producing 100% non-defectives. For one thing, the mean is offset from the nominal and secondly, the spread is wider than the specified tolerance.

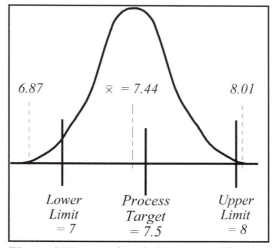

**Figure 55** Process in relation to specification

*Process Capability Index*

A Cpk value, called the process capability index, may also be helpful as this takes into account the *accuracy*, i.e. the location of the mean, of the process.

$$Cpk = \frac{UL - \overline{x}}{3\sigma} \text{ or } \frac{\overline{x} - LL}{3\sigma} \qquad \textbf{(8)}$$

whichever is the smaller.

As with the Cp, the Cpk must be greater than 1 to avoid defectives being produced.

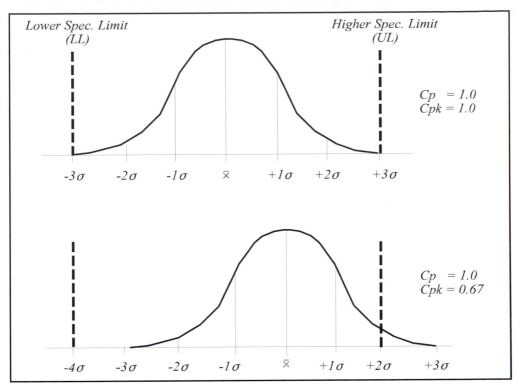

**Figure 56** Process Capability Indices

At this stage, a basic knowledge of capability will suffice - see the following examples. Long term movement and variation of the process is possible and further control of processes will be discussed later.

# Process Capability Studies

## Examples

### Example 1

$$\text{Specification} \quad = \quad 1000 \pm 50$$

$$\sigma \quad = \quad 20 \text{ units}$$

Assuming a stable process, which has been adjusted to be central between the specified limits, calculate the Cp and Cpk.

$$\text{Tolerance} \quad = \quad 100 \text{ units}$$

$$Cp \quad = \quad \frac{100}{6 \times 20} \quad = \quad 0.83$$

i.e. process is not capable of meeting the specification, rejects will be inevitable.

### Process Capability (Cpk)

$$Cpk \quad = \quad \frac{\text{upper limit - mean}}{3\sigma} \quad \text{or} \quad \frac{\text{mean - lower limit}}{3\sigma}$$

whichever is the smaller.

$$Cpk \quad = \quad \frac{50}{3 \times 20} \quad = \quad 0.83$$

Note, since the process is assumed to be central, Cpk is equal to Cp, i.e. 0.83

Example 2.

Specification = 115±5

$\overline{X}$ = 112 units

σ = 1 unit

Calculate Cp and Cpk.

Cp = $\dfrac{10}{6 \times 1}$ = 1.67

Cpk = $\dfrac{112 - 110}{3 \times 1}$ = 0.67

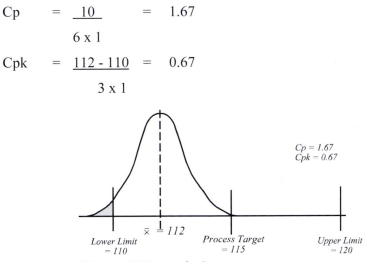

Cp = 1.67
Cpk = 0.67

$\overline{x}$ = 112

Lower Limit
= 110

Process Target
= 115

Upper Limit
= 120

**Figure 57** Example 2

Process is capable but requires adjustment

Example 3

UL = 50 units, LL = 45 units

σ = 0.2 units, x̄ = 48.5 units

Calculate Cp and Cpk.

$$Cp = \frac{5}{6 \times 0.2} = 4.17$$

$$Cpk = \frac{50 - 48.5}{3 \times 0.2} = 2.5$$

therefore process is capable

Example 4

Target value          =   6 units

Tolerance             =   ±6 units

Process mean  $\overline{X}$  =   6 units

Process sigma  σ   =   2 units

Calculate Cp and Cpk.

Cp      =   $\dfrac{\text{Tolerance}}{6\sigma}$  =  $\dfrac{12}{6 \times 2}$   =  1        therefore process is capable

Cpk    =   $\dfrac{\text{upper limit - mean}}{3\sigma}$        or   $\dfrac{\text{mean - lower limit}}{3\sigma}$

whichever is the smaller.

Cpk    =   $\dfrac{12 - 6}{3 \times 2}$   =  1   or   $\dfrac{6 - 0}{3 \times 2}$   =  1   therefore process is set correctly

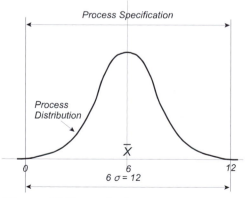

**Figure 58** Example 4

178

Example 5

| | | | |
|---|---|---|---|
| Target value | | = | 5 units |
| Tolerance | | = | ±5 units |
| Process mean | $\bar{X}$ = | | 7 units |
| Process sigma | $\sigma$ = | | 1.67 units |

Calculate Cp and Cpk.

Cp $= \dfrac{\text{Tolerance}}{6\sigma} = \dfrac{10}{6 \times 1.67} = 1$    therefore process is capable

Cpk $= \dfrac{\text{upper limit - mean}}{3\sigma}$   or   $\dfrac{\text{mean - lower limit}}{3\sigma}$

whichever is the smaller.

Cpk $= \dfrac{10 - 7}{3 \times 1.67} = 0.6$   or   $\dfrac{7 - 0}{3 \times 1.67} = 1.397$

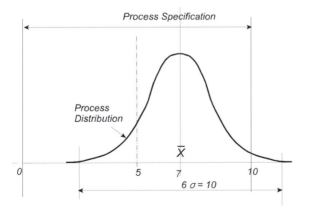

**Figure 59** Example 5

therefore process is not set correctly

Example 6

Target value         =  3 units

Tolerance            =  ±3 units

Process mean  $\overline{X}$  =  3 units

Process sigma  σ  =  3 units

Calculate Cp and Cpk.

Cp   =  $\dfrac{\text{Tolerance}}{6\sigma}$  =  $\dfrac{6}{6 \times 3}$  =  0.33   therefore process is not capable

Cpk  =     $\dfrac{\text{upper limit - mean}}{3\sigma}$   or   $\dfrac{\text{mean - lower limit}}{3\sigma}$

whichever is the smaller.

Cpk    =  $\dfrac{6-3}{3 \times 3}$  =  0.33   or  $\dfrac{3-0}{3 \times 3}$  =  0.33

therefore process is set correctly since Cpk = Cp

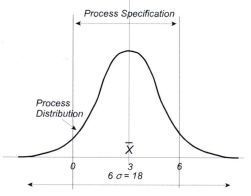

**Figure 60** Example 6

**The Specification, Measurement and Process Capability relationship**

Since measurement is itself a process, it will have its own process capability. This is referred to as the uncertainty of measurement. The relationship between the process capability and the uncertainty of measurement may be appreciated in the following graphical representation.

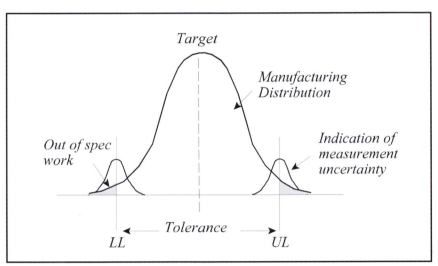

**Figure 61** Uncertainty of measurement

A number of important features may be observed:

a)    The specification is the working tolerance with associated upper and lower limits.

b)    Capability is the relationship between the tolerance and manufacturing distribution given as Cp or Cpk from which the areas in the tails of distribution may be calculated giving out of spec work.

c)    Measurement uncertainty results in inspection error - passing defective work and failing adequate work. To ensure this error is minimal, a ratio of 10:1 between the working tolerance and measurement uncertainty is desirable.

## Statistical Process Control

In-process inspection means monitoring the process during production by periodically inspecting samples and plotting the results on a chart. This is called Statistical Process Control or SPC for short.

The two types of variation have already been referred to above. SPC is the application of statistics to help distinguish between variations due to common causes and those due to special causes. If variations due to special causes occur then the process is said to be out of statistical control. If action is not taken as soon as special cause variations are indicated then rejects will occur.

The method used for SPC is the control chart. Using the results of a process capability study, control limits are calculated within which all results should lie according to the rules referred to earlier. The control chart is based on the principle that the chance of a point lying outside the control limits due to common causes is very remote and such a point is, therefore, indicative of a special cause being present. It is, therefore, a signal to investigate the circumstances of the process to determine the reason for the special cause, to correct the condition and to identify the necessary action to prevent it from recurring in future. This may require the use of problem solving techniques such as cause-effect analysis and brain-storming which are covered later in this book. Statistical Process Control (SPC) is the monitoring and analysis of process conditions using statistical techniques to determine accurately process performance and preventive or corrective actions required.

The statistical techniques involved in SPC have been around for a long time, with the Shewhart control chart, designed in 1923, being little different from the type of chart in regular use today. American industry used the procedure during the Second World War in the manufacture of armaments and a British Standard entitled "Control Chart Technique" was issued in 1935. However, it is considered by many that the adoption by the Japanese of the system is the basis of their obvious success in achieving economical production. Many companies in the UK and elsewhere, have embraced the concepts of SPC for purely economic reasons. Unfortunately, at the time of writing, 50% of mass production in the UK has no statistical control element at all. In 35% of cases, adjustment is manually operated and only 15% is controlled automatically using closed-loop principles. Although the theoretical concepts of SPC have been widely available for over forty years, relatively few companies have taken advantage of them until recently. In the 80s, the Automobile industry, specifically the Ford Motor

182

# Introduction to Quality

Company, accelerated the application of the principles of SPC by insisting that all their contract firms adopt the concepts. Indeed they form part of QS 9000. The emphasis by the auto manufacturers started around 1983 and at the time some industries felt the technique was applicable only to precision engineering parts produced in large volume. Foremost amongst these were the rubber and foundry industries. This illustrated a lack of understanding of the technique and benefits that are available to those prepared to investigate and make the necessary changes. Unfortunately, the failure to appreciate the concepts at management level is widespread, with many organisations having little understanding of the requirements. Companies are putting systems in because their customers are demanding it, rather than from an appreciation of the benefits from their own viewpoint.

To contrast SPC and non-SPC situations, the classic study of MAZDA gearboxes provides an illustration. Some years ago, the Ford Motor Company, who have a 25% stake in Mazda, carried out a study between an American and a Japanese company manufacturing gearboxes to the same specification. The American company had twice the failure rate in the gearboxes compared to the Japanese company. On disassembling twenty gearboxes from each company and measuring the components part, it was discovered that elements from the Japanese organisation used only some 20% of the tolerance zone specified. In fact, so consistent were the measurements that it was first thought that the measuring equipment had broken down.

On the other hand, the American company's components used the whole of the tolerance zone. Whilst still being within the limits, this meant that assemblies would be outside specifications far more quickly than their Japanese counterparts. Hence, the higher failure rate encountered.

The benefits of successful implementation are many and far-reaching. Motivation is not only a pre-condition of this success but it is a product of it. A motivation cycle can be created which will improve individual, group, department and company performance as a whole. Considerable reductions in rework costs and an almost total elimination of scrap are not unusual when SPC is operating effectively. It provides a knowledge of machine and process capability and performance, enabling the engineer to make confident decisions about equipment requirements, preventive maintenance actions and scheduling, corrective actions and cures. Prevention rather than cure is not only an important quality assurance philosophy but is the very nature of SPC. It can, therefore, reduce not only rework inspection but also first time inspection and associated costs.

## Principles of Statistical Process Control Charts

SPC is intended to:

a)      ensure that the process remains stable, i.e. does not deteriorate with respect to accuracy (location) or precision (spread).

b)      provide evidence of potential means of improving the process.

To do this every item could be measured as it is made and plotted on a chart. If the specified limits have been drawn on the chart then it could be seen if the items were within specification. Using SPC it is not necessary to measure and plot every item. Monitoring the mean and spread of samples taken at regular intervals should provide sufficient indication of any trend away from stability. In fact, monitoring sample parameters provides more sensitive information than 100% inspection. Trends are more apparent.

## Variable Charts

A study was carried out for a variable specified as $14\pm5$ units. For illustration, 100 items were measured and grouped into subgroups of five with the following results:

| Sample | 1 | 2 | 3 | 4 | 5 | 6 | 7 | 8 | 9 | 10 | 11 | 12 | 13 | 14 | 15 | 16 | 17 | 18 | 19 | 20 |
|---|---|---|---|---|---|---|---|---|---|---|---|---|---|---|---|---|---|---|---|---|
| x1 | 13 | 15 | 14 | 14 | 13 | 13 | 15 | 12 | 14 | 14 | 12 | 15 | 13 | 14 | 16 | 13 | 15 | 12 | 14 | 14 |
| x2 | 13 | 16 | 14 | 15 | 12 | 13 | 12 | 14 | 13 | 13 | 13 | 16 | 13 | 15 | 12 | 13 | 14 | 13 | 13 | 16 |
| x3 | 14 | 12 | 13 | 13 | 14 | 12 | 13 | 15 | 13 | 17 | 15 | 15 | 14 | 13 | 16 | 15 | 15 | 14 | 14 | 13 |
| x4 | 14 | 14 | 9 | 14 | 15 | 12 | 15 | 13 | 14 | 13 | 14 | 14 | 14 | 14 | 15 | 11 | 16 | 16 | | 14 |
| x5 | 13 | 14 | 13 | 14 | 15 | 15 | 17 | 14 | 15 | 13 | 15 | 15 | 14 | 13 | 13 | 14 | 12 | 13 | 13 | 13 |
| Mean | 13.4 | 14.2 | 12.6 | 14 | 13.8 | 13 | 14.4 | 13.6 | 13.8 | 14 | 13.8 | 15 | 13.6 | 14 | 14.2 | 14 | 13.4 | 13.6 | 14 | 14 |
| Range[1] (w) | 1 | 4 | 5 | 2 | 3 | 3 | 5 | 3 | 2 | 4 | 3 | 2 | 1 | 2 | 4 | 2 | 4 | 4 | 3 | 3 |

---

[15]      The range of a sample is the difference between the largest and smallest values in the sample. Some users prefer the symbol R to w for the sample range. w has been used here to avoid confusion when referring to Murdoch and Barnes' Statistical Tables.

# Introduction to Quality

$$mean\ \bar{\bar{x}}\ =\ 13.81\ \sigma = 1.286$$

Note: $\bar{\bar{x}}$ denotes the grand mean of all the data in the table while $\bar{x}$ denotes the mean of a single sample of five items.

Plotting the individual values:

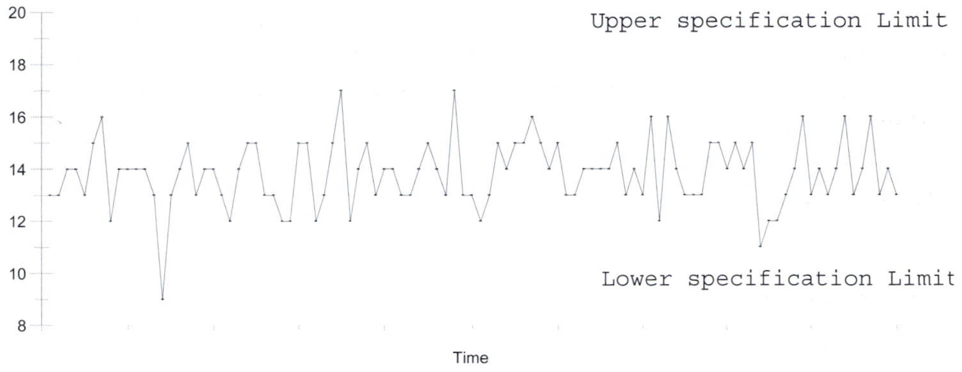

Figure 62 Plot of individual data

Now plotting the sample means (the average of each group of five items):

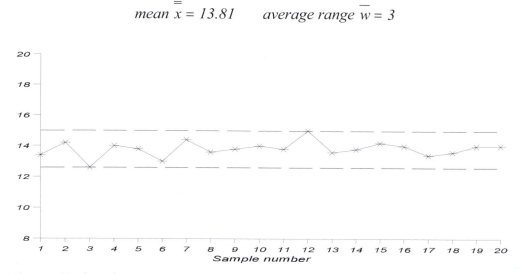

$$mean\ \overline{\overline{x}} = 13.81 \qquad average\ range\ \overline{w} = 3$$

**Figure 63** Plot of sample means

It can be seen from the above that the spread of the distribution of the sample means that it is not as great as for individual values. This is to be expected since samples are tending to cancel out individual variations. This is the key to control charts.

It can be shown that the relationship between the distributions of the sample means and the individual values is $1/\sqrt{n}$ i.e. $s = \sigma/\sqrt{n}$

Where 's' is the standard error or the standard deviation of the sample means.

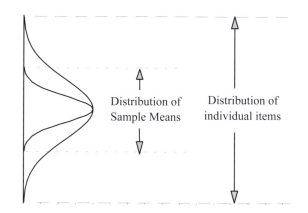

Control limits are set at the position corresponding to a probability of one in a thousand (0.001) which is ±3.09s. For manual calculations this is usually rounded to ±3s.

**Figure 64** Distribution of means and items

186

Therefore, the upper and lower control limits of the means chart will be:

$$Upper\ Control\ Limit\ (UCL) = \bar{\bar{x}} + 3\frac{\sigma}{\sqrt{n}}$$

$$Lower\ Control\ Limit\ (LCL) = \bar{\bar{x}} - 3\frac{\sigma}{\sqrt{n}}$$

(9)

These formulae are the basis of all control charts where the data forms a normal distribution.

Further, for variables, it can be shown that there is a direct relationship between the average range of samples and the distribution from which they are drawn. $\sigma$ is therefore often estimated from the average range using the constant $d_n$ in table 12, where n is the sample size.

$$\sigma \approx \frac{\bar{w}}{d_n}$$

(10)

**Table 12** Control Chart Constants

| n | 2 | 3 | 4 | 5 | 6 | 7 | 8 | 9 | 10 |
|---|---|---|---|---|---|---|---|---|---|
| $d_n$ | 1.13 | 1.69 | 2.06 | 2.33 | 2.53 | 2.7 | 2.85 | 2.97 | 3.08 |
| A'0.001 | 1.937 | 1.054 | 0.75 | 0.594 | 0.498 | 0.432 | 0.384 | 0.347 | 0.317 |
| A'0.025 | 1.229 | 0.668 | 0.476 | 0.377 | 0.316 | 0.274 | 0.244 | 0.22 | 0.202 |
| D'0.999 | 0 | 0.04 | 0.1 | 0.16 | 0.21 | 0.26 | 0.29 | 0.32 | 0.35 |
| D'0.975 | 0.04 | 0.18 | 0.29 | 0.37 | 0.42 | 0.46 | 0.5 | 0.52 | 0.54 |
| D'0.025 | 2.81 | 2.17 | 1.93 | 1.81 | 1.72 | 1.66 | 1.62 | 1.58 | 1.56 |
| D'0.001 | 4.12 | 2.98 | 2.57 | 2.34 | 2.21 | 2.11 | 2.04 | 1.99 | 1.93 |

# Statistical Process Control

Thus:

$$Upper\ Control\ Limit\ (UCL) = \overline{\overline{x}} + 3\frac{\overline{w}}{d_n\sqrt{n}}$$

$$Lower\ Control\ Limit\ (LCL) = \overline{\overline{x}} - 3\frac{\overline{w}}{d_n\sqrt{n}} \tag{11}$$

Now as a given sample size n and $d_n$ are constant along with $\sqrt{n}$ and 3.09 (and the constant is calculated and listed in statistical tables the correct value is used rather than 3) these can be replaced with one constant $A'_{0.001}$ thus:

$$Upper\ Control\ Limit\ (UCL) = \overline{\overline{x}} + A'_{0.001}\ \overline{w}$$

$$Lower\ Control\ Limit\ (LCL) = \overline{\overline{x}} - A'_{0.001}\ \overline{w} \tag{12}$$

These control limits are referred to as the **Action Limits**. Since the occurrence of a value outside these limits is only likely to happen by chance - one in a thousand times, it is more probable that the process has shifted and, therefore, requires immediate action to prevent work being produced outside the specification limits.

In addition to the Action Limits, it is common to find **Warning Limits** in use. These are set at 2s instead of 3s (or more strictly speaking 1.96s) which corresponds to a probability of one in 40 or 0.025 thus:

$$Upper\ Warning\ Limit\ (UCL) = \overline{\overline{x}} + A'_{0.025}\ \overline{w}$$

$$Lower\ Warning\ Limit\ (LCL) = \overline{\overline{x}} - A'_{0.025}\ \overline{w} \tag{13}$$

The values of these constants may be found in **Table 12** above and statistical tables such as Murdoch & Barnes.

Hence for the above example where:

$$mean\ \bar{\bar{x}} = 13.81 \qquad average\ range\ \bar{w} = 3$$

the control limits would be:

$$UCL = 13.81 + 0.594 \times 3$$
$$= 15.59$$
$$LCL = 13.81 - 0.594 \times 3$$
$$= 12.03$$
$$UWL = 13.81 + 0.377 \times 3$$
$$= 14.94$$
$$LWL = 13.81 - 0.377 \times 3$$
$$= 12.68$$

The Control Chart would look like this:

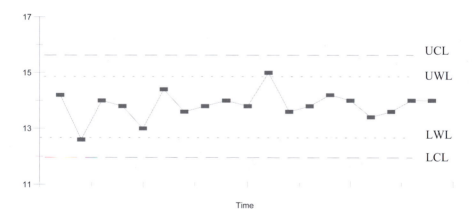

**Figure 65** Control chart sample means

The fact that two values lie at the warning limits is not unusual since this can be expected to happen with 1 in 40 results, i.e. 0.025 is the probability of a value lying outside 2 standard deviations from the mean.

# Statistical Process Control

## *Sample Range Chart*

In addition to the Sample Means Chart, the spread of the distribution can be monitored by plotting a chart of the sample ranges. The construction of the chart is similar to that for the means chart but this time the average range is used. However, the distribution of ranges is zero limited, i.e. it cannot be less than zero. Therefore, the distribution may not be normal for small values of w. For this reason, rather than calculating the limits from first principles tables are used.

Table 12 provides the respective values.

Thus for a sample size of 5 there are four constants:

$D'_{0.999} = 0.16$, $D'_{0.975} = 0.37$, $D'_{0.025} = 1.81$ and $D'_{0.001} = 2.34$

The respective control limits are obtained by simply multiplying the average range by each of these values.

For the previous example they are:

$$UAL = 2.34 \times 3$$
$$= 7.02$$
$$UWL = 1.81 \times 3$$
$$= 5.43$$
$$LWL = 0.37 \times 3$$
$$= 1.11$$
$$LAL = 0.16 \times 3$$
$$= 0.48$$

The Range Chart would, therefore, look like this:

**Figure 66** Control chart for sample range

Notice, low values are OK since they indicate higher precision, less spread. For this reason, the lower control limits are not always used.

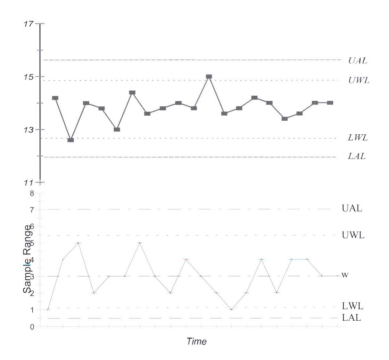

**Figure 67** Combined sample means and range chart

Very often, the sample means chart and range chart are constructed one above the other so that both the accuracy and precision can be monitored at the same time.

191

# Statistical Process Control

## Attribute Charts

The previous section described the procedure to be observed when Statistical Quality Control (SQC) is applied to variable data. In many inspection situations the data which is available about a process is not in the form of measured variables but in the form of counts such as the number of defects or defectives. This section shows how to apply SQC when attribute data is collected.

The two types of attribute data lead to the use of two types of control charts:

1.        Charts for defectives

2.        Charts for defects

These are further split into two charts, one for the situation in which the sample size is constant and one for samples of varying size, hence the set of charts available for attributes becomes:

        a)        number of defective units per sub-group

        b)        proportion of defective units per sub-group

        c)        number of defects per sub-group

        d)        number of defects per unit

The principles of control charts for attributes is exactly the same as for variables, i.e. the control limits are set at the process average $\pm 3\sigma$ where $\sigma$ is the standard deviation of the respective distribution. By plotting the inspection results, changes in the process average may be observed. Note, for attributes inspection a sub-group equates to a sample in variables. However, it usually means 100% inspection suitably divided into convenient sub-groups. It is the number of items inspected during a suitable period of production. The number of items in each sample should preferably remain constant (although this is not essential). The interval between each sample should be chosen on the basis of production frequency, the importance of the operation or process. The samples need to be sufficiently large to allow defectives to appear (although hopefully none). The samples should be taken from one process otherwise it will be difficult to identify the source or cause of any defectives, i.e. separate charts should be kept for different processes.

# Introduction to Quality

The respective means and standard deviations for attributes charts are:

| Type of attribute | Mean | Standard Deviation (σ) |
|---|---|---|
| Number of defectives | $\overline{np}$ | $\sqrt{(\overline{np}(1 - \frac{\overline{np}}{n}))}$ |
| Proportion of defectives | $\overline{p}$ | $\sqrt{\frac{\overline{p}(1-\overline{p})}{n}}$ |
| Number of defects | $\overline{c}$ | $\sqrt{c}$ |
| Number of defects per unit | $\overline{u}$ | $\sqrt{\frac{u}{n}}$ |

## The np chart for number of defectives

a)　the sub-group is constant, i.e. defectives per hour or per shift where the rate of production is constant or results are recorded say, for every 50 units.

b)　the number of defectives is meaningful, ie. not all units are defective and employees understand what period or sub-group the number of defectives is based on.

$\overline{np}$ is the average number of defectives derived from a number of observed periods or sub-groups over a period of time.

$$\overline{np} = \frac{Total\ number\ of\ defective\ items}{Total\ number\ of\ items\ made\ during\ period} \qquad (15)$$

The control limits for attributes charts are calculated in the same way as for variables charts using appropriate means and standard deviations.

Thus for a number defective chart the control limits would be:

$$Control\ Limits\ =\ \overline{np}\ \pm\ 3\ \sqrt{\overline{np}(1 - \frac{\overline{np}}{\overline{n}})} \qquad (16)$$

**The p chart for proportion of defectives**

This chart is similar to the number of defectives chart except that it can be used when the sample size is not constant and/or the proportion of defectives is more meaningful than the absolute number of defectives.

The process average is calculated which is the total number of defectives divided by the total number inspected over a period of time.

$$\overline{p}\ =\ \frac{Total\ number\ of\ defective\ items}{Total\ number\ inspected}$$

$$Mean\ subgroup\ size\ =\ \frac{Total\ number\ produced}{Number\ of\ subgroups}$$

$$Control\ Limits\ =\ \overline{p}\ \pm\ 3\ \sqrt{\frac{\overline{p}(1 - \overline{p})}{\overline{n}}}$$

If the sub-group varies by more than 25% from the mean sub-group size, then the control limits have to be calculated for that subgroup. Otherwise, it is acceptable to base the control limits on the mean subgroup size $\overline{n}$.

# Introduction to Quality

## The c chart for number of defects

The c chart is used for monitoring defects where:

a)    the average subgroup size is constant or can be made so,

b)    the average rate of defects can be expressed as a number,

c)    there are sufficient numbers of defects per subgroup to record

A c chart would be appropriate in the following situations:

1.    Continuous production. For example, flaws per 100 metres of extruded section,

2.    Daily number of defects recorded by a department. This could include defects of any kind totalled together,

3.    Number of defects per finished item. For example, total number of non-conformities per fridge found at final inspection and test.

The average number of defects is $\bar{c}$

$$\bar{c} = \frac{Total\ number\ of\ defects}{Total\ number\ of\ subgroup\ inspected}$$

$$\bar{c} = \frac{c1\ +\ c2\ +\ c3\ + c3\ ....\ \ cm}{m}$$

where m is total number of subgroups

$$Control\ Limits\ =\ \bar{c}\ \pm\ 3\sqrt{c}$$

## The u chart for number of defects per unit

This chart is similar to the c chart and is used in the same situations except that it can be used where the natural subgroup size varies, for example when the number manufactured per day would not be sufficient to record on a c chart, i.e. where the number of defects per subgroup is often zero. In the case of the u chart the "unit" may include more than one item or period of production in order that the number of defects per unit is recordable.

The average number of defects per unit is $\bar{u}$

$$\bar{u} = \frac{Total\ number\ of\ defects}{Total\ number\ of\ units\ inspected}$$

$$\sigma = \sqrt{(\bar{u}/n)}$$

$$Control\ Limits = \bar{u} \pm 3\sqrt{(\bar{u}/n)}$$

## Selection of control charts

Various types of chart are available. Described below are some of the more commonly used charts, together with examples of where the charts can be usefully employed. See **Figure 68**.

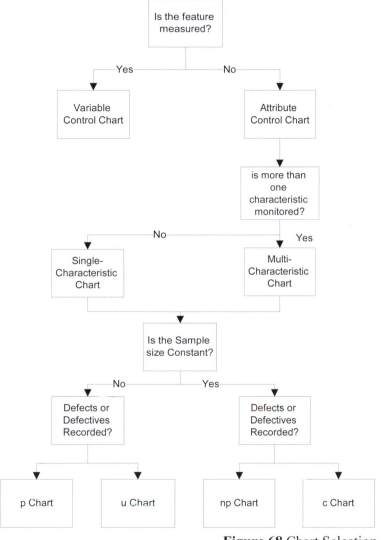

**Figure 68** Chart Selection

# Statistical Process Control

**Variable data:** X/R Charts (Average and Range). These charts will be used when the data is measured, i.e. readings from measuring device such as a volt-meter.

**Attribute data:** Single characteristic chart or Multiple characteristic chart. These charts will be used in go/nogo, pass/fail situations.

i.     The p chart for proportion of defectives where the sample is not necessarily of constant size.

ii.    The np chart for number of defectives where the sample size is constant.

iii.   The c chart for number of defects where sample size is constant.

iv.    The u chart for number of defects per unit where the sample size is not necessarily constant.

**Table 13** Attribute Chart Selection

| Sample size varies | Sample size constant | Fault type | Description |
|---|---|---|---|
| Proportion | Number | | |
| p | np | Defectives | Accept or Reject |
| u | c | Defects | Number of different flaws |

Examples in the use of single characteristic charts may be:

For p and np types charts:

- ○    pass or fail light bulb test
- ○    go or no-go hole size
- ○    correct or incorrect torque loading
- ○    accept or reject weld strength

For c or u type charts:

- ○ porosity or number of holes in a casting

- ○ number of paint blemishes on a panel

- ○ number of flaws in a sheet of glass

- ○ number of errors on a printed circuit board

- ○ number of faults with a washing machine

In the latter two examples, printed circuit board and washing machine, each board or machine may contain various defects. In the case of the printed circuit board, the characteristics could be: a component missing, bad soldering, wrong component, defective components, or in the case of the washing machine, leaking, fails to start, motor defective, heater defective etc. In these circumstances, it may be appropriate to employ a multiple characteristic chart. With this type of chart, each of the above characteristics will be monitored individually. The result of this monitoring is then collated and the total number of defects is plotted.

### *Advantages of Using Variables*

1. Small samples (e.g. five items) are sufficient to keep a check on both process average and variability.

2. Gradual changes such as drifts can be detected and the process reset *before* it goes out of specification limit. Changes in variability can be detected on the range chart.

3. Sudden changes in process average and variability can also be detected but where this results in all work being out of specification limit, attributes will do this equally well.

### *Advantages of Using Attributes*

1. Many qualities cannot be measured conveniently as variables, e.g. appearance, taste etc., although some attributes, for example sweetness, are often estimated on a scale of say 0 to 5.

2. Attributes are usually easier to check and require a less skilled inspector.

3.     Several types of defective can be observed and plotted together as total number rejected, but the chart should always include an analysis, so that types which often occur can be identified and investigated.

4.     Sample sizes for attributes are much larger than for variables. For example, if the scrap from a process averages 1%, a sample of 100 is needed to have an average chance of finding one reject in it and rather more to give a good chance of doing so. Samples can, and sometimes are, taken specifically to provide data for an attribute chart, but in the majority of cases we use data from 100% inspection which is being performed anyway.

# Introduction to Quality

## Control Charts and Decision Lines

Once process capability has been established and accepted, the control charts need to be set up to enable monitoring of the process, with a view to maintaining quality over long periods. Since there are two ways that processes may vary - range and mean - it is necessary to set-up two separate control charts. As with capability studies, the use of tables and set procedures will simplify the operation of control chart construction without becoming heavily involved with statistical theoretical concepts.

## Setting up of Control Charts

### *Procedure:*

1.  Take an initial 'first-off' sample of at least 10 items and inspect to confirm the process is set up correctly.

    *It may be possible to carry out a mini capability study by inspecting a further 15 consecutive items.*

2.  A **Pre-Control Chart** can now be set up using control limits calculated from the capability study, or if this is not expedient they should be set in from the specification limits by 25% of the tolerance.

3.  Proceed to monitor the process by taking samples at suitable intervals, say, every hour or every 50 components, and plot them on the chart.

    *It will usually be necessary to experiment with sample intervals until a reliable interval has been confidently established. There is no point in taking samples every hour if process drift takes several days to deteriorate. On the other hand, too long an interval may mean that the process has shifted before the next sample is due. Process stability clearly affects this. Some processes are inherently stable, such as press tools and dies, others are more sensitive such as oven temperatures or automatic fillers. Other considerations might be the criticality or the effect of process changes. Small changes in some processes may have little impact on the finished product, in other cases they may have devastating results.*

*It is sometimes a mistake for samples to be taken at the same times every day as there may be cyclical errors occurring which fall between samples.*

4.      After approximately 20 samples the control limits should be re-calculated and the control chart revised; continue taking samples, plotting them on the chart, interpreting the results and taking corrective action.

5.      Apart from their appearance on pre-control charts, it is not necessary to draw the specification limits on the control charts. Regular Cp and Cpk verification should be carried out and checks made from plotted values to see whether the process is under statistical control. If specification limits are drawn on the chart, then the process should be well within specification limits.

6.      Where doubt exists regarding a plotted value such as a freak or rogue value, a note must always be made with respect to possible causes. Further samples may be taken immediately. In any event the chart should be annotated whenever there is a change in the process such as change of tool, material, shift, operator etc.

*Control charts for attributes*

Process control can be exercised using these simple charts on which the number or proportion of defectives, or the number of defects or defects per unit are plotted. Before commencing to do this, however, it is absolutely vital to clarify what constitutes a defective and what is meant by a defect. No process control technique can survive the heated arguments which will surround a badly defined system. It is evident that in the study of attribute data, there will be several degrees of imperfection. The classification of defects is a subject in its own right, but it is clear that a scratch on paintwork or table top surface may range from a deep gouge to a slight mark, hardly visible to the naked eye. To ensure the smooth control of a process using attribute data, it is often necessary to provide representative samples, photographs or other objective evidence to support the decision made. These will allow the attention and the effort to be concentrated on improving the process rather than debating the issues surrounding defect levels.

# Introduction to Quality

As there is no range of values to consider with attributes, only one control chart is necessary.

The chart is set up by calculating the mean number of defectives over a period of time and by using a standard formula ascertaining the control limits. The data will also be plotted to see if the process is in statistical control at the time. Subsequently, values are plotted in the same way as variables, the information being analysed and acted upon.

Where the process is in statistical control the average level of defectives will become the capability of the process and is used as a yardstick by which improvement may be made.

*Sample size and frequency of sampling*

As the attribute chart is particularly useful where 100 per cent inspection is being done, the question of a sample size does not always arise. When samples are taken however, we must think in terms of much larger samples than we would use for variables and, curiously enough, the better the average quality the larger the sample size. Thus, suppose that about ten per cent of our production is usually defective. Now that it is one defective in 10, so that if a sample of, say, 20 is taken, on average two defectives per sample would be expected.

Suppose, however, the quality is improved so that only one per cent of our production is defective. Now that is only one defective in 100 and, therefore, a sample of 20 would be useless. It would only average one defective in every five samples. A sample of nearer 200 would be needed. As a general guide, the sample taken, must be large enough to give a small percentage of defectives to plot.

Practical considerations usually decide the frequency of inspection. Work is often produced in batches and, therefore, one sample per batch can be taken. If production is continuous, then each morning or afternoon may be treated as a batch, or make one's shift work into a batch, and so on. The principle of sampling as often as is reasonably practicable still holds. Indeed one of the disadvantages of taking a day's production as the sample is that the whole lot may be wrong before the chart draws attention to it.

# Statistical Process Control

*Example*

Consider a company making jam tarts: What may be wrong with a jam tart?

1.  Under filled with jam.

2.  Over filled with jam.

3.  Crust broken.

4.  Burnt.

5.  Underdone.

Suppose they are manufactured in batches of 300.

Inspectors will determine on a basis of 'attributes' if the tarts are passed or failed individually. If the proportion defectives in each batch (n) is 'p', e.g. 0.01, then the number of defectives in each batch will be $np$, e.g. 300 x 0.01 = 3. Long term, the average $np$ may be calculated and a number attribute control chart drawn up with control limits based upon $\sigma = \sqrt{npq}$, the spread of defectives approximating to a normal distribution.

Attribute failures tend to follow a Poisson or binomial distribution, which in application approximate to a normal distribution.

For example, consider a sample of 300 items; components on a printed circuit board (PCB), jam tarts, soldered joints, rivets, welds, chocolate bars.

If the probability of each being good is, say, 0.98, i.e. q = 0.98.

Then the probability of each being bad is 1 - 0.98 = 0.02.

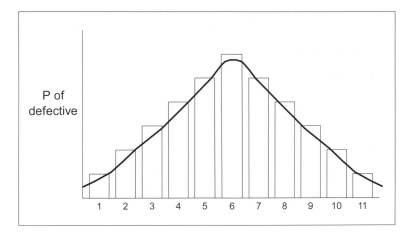

**Figure 69** Expanded binomial equation

If the binomial equation $(q + p)^{300}$ is expanded a series is produced which, when substituting the values for q and p would plot out to an approximate normal distribution.

Probabilities beyond 11 would be negligible.

Thus it may be concluded that a control chart may be set up similar to a variables means chart.

### *Proportion defective charts (p chart)*

The p chart is used when dealing with defectives (e.g. scrap or rejects), and the sample size varies. In almost any production shop, the number produced varies slightly from day-to-day, so if the results of 100% inspection of daily production are monitored by a control chart, the 'sample' size varies correspondingly. The steps to set up this chart are in principle the same as used for variables charts.

## Number defective (np) charts BS 5701

Probably a simpler way of plotting control limits on number defective control charts is to use the tables in BS 5701. There follows a worked example from the standard including the use of the special tables.

## The first control chart

a)      For the first trial of a number defective quality control chart, select a process that can be expected to give reasonably continuous production and that produces output containing an expected proportion of defectives in the range 1% to 10%.

b)      Select samples each of 25 items (or of 50 items if the general level of defectives in the product is 5% or less and the rate of production permits) from the most suitable point in the process. The interval between samples should be such that approximately 5% of the product is selected for examination.

c)      Examine each item, note the number of defective specimens in each sample and record this number in the order in which the samples were taken, on a control chart as shown in **Figure 70**.

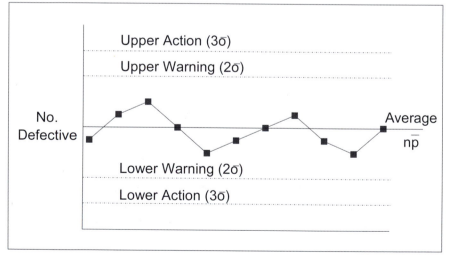

**Figure 70** Control chart with action limits

**Example:**

(i)      When the results from 25 samples (each of 25 or 50 items) have been plotted in this way, find the control limit, as shown below, and mark it boldly as a broken line on the control chart.

To find the control limit:

(1)      calculate the average number of defective items ('defectives') per sample in these 25 samples.

(2)      refer to the table, the control limit will be shown against the average number of defectives per sample.

(ii)      For example, the following results of the first 25 samples, each of 50 items, taken from a production unit might be:

(1)      Number of defectives found per sample = 1, 0, 3, 0, 3, 2, 0, 2, 0, 2, 0, 1, 1, 0, 2, 5, 3, 1, 1, 2, 0, 2, 1, 1, 3.

then:

$$\text{Average number of defectives} = \frac{36}{25} = 1.44 \text{ per sample}$$

(2)      On referring to the table below (see BS 5701 for full details), the control limit given for 1.53 (i.e. the number in the table next greater than the calculated number) defectives per sample is 5.7 and a broken line is placed on the chart at 5.7 defectives in a sample.

| Average number of defectives expected per sample | 0.1 | 0.33 | 0.67 | 1.08 | 1.53 | 2.04 | 2.57 | 3.13 | 3.72 |
|---|---|---|---|---|---|---|---|---|---|
| Upper Control limit | 1.7 | 2.7 | 3.7 | 4.7 | 5.7 | 6.7 | 7.7 | 8.7 | 9.7 |
| Upper Warning limit | 0.7 | 1.7 | 2.7 | 3.7 | 4.7 | 5.7 | 6.7 | 7.7 | 8.7 |

When the control limit has been placed on the chart, continue to select and examine samples, as before, recording on the chart the number of defectives found in each sample. While these recorded results remain below the control limit, variations in results should be ignored as being due to chance, and confidence may be felt that the quality of the product is not deteriorating. There is the separate question of whether this quality is satisfactory, and the states of 'in statistical control' and 'satisfactory production quality' should not be confused.

It is recommended that annotations should be made at the appropriate places on the chart to indicate occurrences of technical importance such as machine adjustment, tool replacement, change of operator, fresh supply of raw material, etc., as these notes will help the correct appraisement of trouble if results fall outside limit values.

If a result falls beyond the control limit it is a signal that the quality of the product has deteriorated and that immediate corrective action is required. If, moreover, results that usually fall below the control limit approach it and cluster near it, this is also an indication of a deterioration in quality which, if unchecked, is likely to become serious. To make this indication simpler to detect, a warning limit may be set one unit below the control limit. The presence of several points between these limits in a short period of time can be used to signal the need for investigation.

Below are some worked examples of calculating the mean and the upper and lower control limits.

a)     The sampled size varied but not more than ±25%[16] and on average was 500. From a total of 12000 sampled, 400 defectives were found.

The proportion of defectives is p i.e. the number of defectives (np) divided by the number in the sample.

$$\bar{p} = \frac{\Sigma np}{\Sigma n} \tag{20}$$

Calculate the average number of defectives for the process:

$$\bar{p} = \frac{Total\ number\ defectives}{Total\ number\ inspected}$$
$$\bar{p} = \frac{400}{12000} = 0.033 \ ' \tag{21}$$

Calculate the Control Limits (UCL, LCL):

$$UCL_p = \bar{p} + 3 * \sqrt{\frac{\bar{p}(1-\bar{p})}{\bar{n}}}$$

$$UCL_p = 0.033 + 3 * \sqrt{\frac{0.033(1-0.033)}{500}} \tag{22}$$

$$UCL_p = 0.033 + 0.024$$
$$UCL_p = 0.057$$
$$LCL_p = 0.033 - 0.024$$
$$LCL_p = 0.009$$

---

[16]     If the sample size had varied more than 25%, then on each occasion the control limits should be recalculated using the sample size of the particular sub-group

b)      100 defectives were found in 25 samples of 60 items.

Calculate the average number of defectives in each sub-group for the process:

$$\overline{np} = \frac{\Sigma np}{m}$$

$$\overline{np} = \frac{100}{25} = 4 \tag{23}$$

*Where m = The number of sub-groups*

Calculate the Control Limits (UCL, LCL):

$$UCL_{np} = \overline{np} + 3 * \sqrt{\overline{np}(1 - \frac{\overline{np}}{n})}$$

$$UCL_{np} = 4 + 3 * \sqrt{4(1 - \frac{4}{60})}$$

$$UCL_{np} = 4 + 5.8 \tag{24}$$

$$UCL_{np} = 9.8$$

$$LCL_{np} = 4 - 5.8$$

$$LCL_{np} = -1.8$$

If the LCL is negative then ignore this control limit since it is not possible to have less than zero defectives.

c)      100 defects were found in ten samples of 25 items.

Calculate the average number of defects in each sub-group for the process:

$$\overline{c} = \frac{\Sigma c}{m}$$

$$\overline{c} = \frac{100}{10} = 10 \tag{25}$$

*Where m = The number of sub-groups*

Calculate the Control Limits (UCL, LCL):

$$
\begin{aligned}
UCL_c &= \bar{c} + 3 * \sqrt{\bar{c}} \\
UCL_c &= 10 + 3 * \sqrt{10} \\
UCL_c &= 10 + 9.49 \\
UCL_c &= 19.49 \\
LCL_c &= 10 - 9.49 \\
LCL_c &= 0.51
\end{aligned}
\tag{26}
$$

d)    The sample size varied but not more than ±25% from a target of 8. From a total of 96 sampled, 192 defects were found..

Calculate the average number of defects in each sub-group for the process:

$$
\begin{aligned}
\bar{u} &= \frac{\Sigma c}{\Sigma n} \\
\bar{u} &= \frac{192}{96} = 2
\end{aligned}
\tag{27}
$$

*'here c = The number of defectives in each sub-grou*

Calculate the Control Limits (UCL, LCL):

$$
\begin{aligned}
UCL_u &= \bar{u} + 3 * \sqrt{\frac{\bar{u}}{n}} \\
UCL_u &= 2 + 3 * \sqrt{\frac{2}{8}} \\
UCL_u &= 2 + 1.5 \\
UCL_u &= 3.5 \\
LCL_u &= 2 - 1.5 \\
LCL_u &= 0.5
\end{aligned}
\tag{28}
$$

# Statistical Process Control

## Implementing Statistical Quality Control

### Benefits of SQC:

○ Monitoring a process by the use of control charts can provide the basis for a process improvement programme.

○ Giving the operators the opportunity to use their abilities to the full in controlling and improving the process performance - (world class performance).

○ Facilitating process improvement for better quality, lower costs and greater productivity.

○ SQC assists communication and discussion regarding the process performance, giving a better understanding of the requirements and processes ability to meet requirements.

Limitations of SQC: Although there are major benefits from the introduction of SQC, there can also be some limitations and problems.

The organisation may operate a piece work scheme which may prevent the operator having the time to complete the control chart. *One solution to this is for the inspector to complete the control chart. This should be avoided at all costs as it defeats one of the main objectives of SQC which is getting the operator involved with the quality of the work produced. The operator needs to be provided with all necessary facilities to perform SQC.*

The operator may not be capable of understanding or using SQC and may not wish to be involved. It isn't possible to gain appropriate commitment from all areas. *If SQC is properly explained then there will be no problems in understanding or gaining commitment. It is only when the reasoning behind SQC is not fully explained that problems will be encountered.*

There will be certain expenditure associated with the introduction of SQC; resources to implement, equipment (measuring, chart holders and charts etc.), additional time completing and analysing the charts, - *but there are savings such as in quality, productivity etc.*

# Introduction to Quality

The process may not be capable of meeting the specification therefore, SQC cannot be applied. *Applying SQC will help identify the reasons for non-capability of the process and assist in establishing conformance to specification.*

The process may have too many features that need control. *Failure Mode and Effects Analysis may assist in identifying the key features that need control. Alternatively, Multi-feature Attribute Charts could be employed.*

This is not applicable on certain processes, i.e. no measurements are taken, only pass or fail. *Attribute control charts can be used for go/nogo situations.*

Implementation consists of three key elements:

STAGE 1:     Gather the data

STAGE 2:     Determine the control limits

STAGE 3:     Data analysis and variation reduction

These three stages are ceaselessly repeated for continuous improvement in process performance.

## Variable Charts and Data

The procedure to be observed when SQC is applied to variable data is described below.

## STAGE 1  Gather the data

Complete the process details on the Statistical Quality Control Chart (see **Figure 71** SQC Chart) using the Statistical Quality Control Chart and from the Process Capability Study determine an appropriate scale for the average 'x' and range 'R'.

A typical variable SQC chart is shown next.

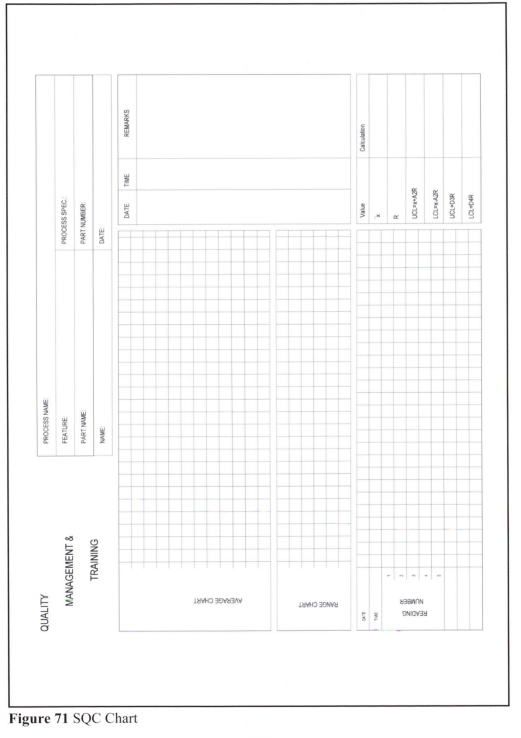

**Figure 71** SQC Chart

For the average and range chart this can be approximately 2 x Process specification.

Obtain first set of readings and record date, time and results. Circle or highlight any readings outside process specification.

Calculate average and range for each sample taken:

$$Average\ \bar{x}\ =\ \frac{\Sigma\ x_i}{n} \qquad (29)$$

Where  $\Sigma x_i$      = the summation of each individual reading 1,2,3,...I

  n        = number of readings

and  R        = range, the difference between the highest and lowest value

Record x bar & R at the bottom of the chart.

$$For\ the\ first\ example\ \bar{x}\ =\ \frac{51.7}{5}\ =\ 10.34$$
$$R\ =\ 10.4\ -\ 10.3\ =\ 0.1 \qquad (30)$$

See **Figure 72** Completed SPC Chart

Plot the value for average and range on the control chart directly above the date and time. Join the points together with a straight line.

Now repeat this exercise until approximately 25 samples or 100 readings have been obtained.

**STAGE 2  Determine the control limits**

A typical completed SQC chart for variables is shown next.

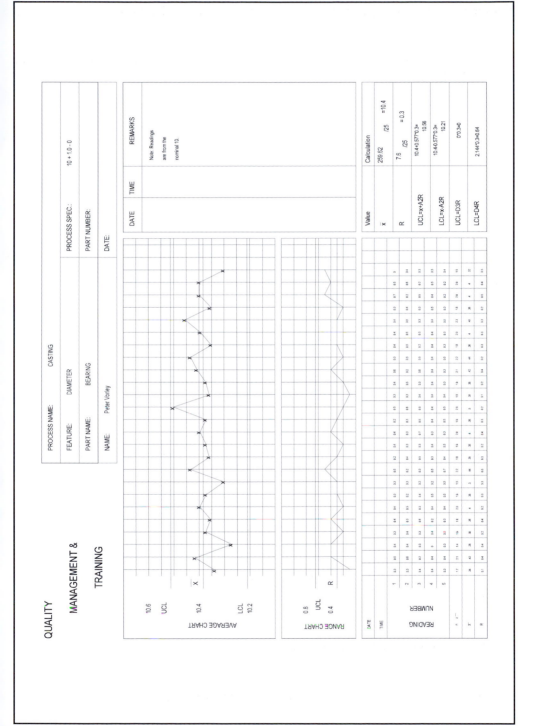

**Figure 72** Completed SQC Chart

Calculate the average range value R.

$$\overline{R} = \frac{\Sigma\ R_i}{k} \tag{31}$$

Where  $\Sigma R_i$   = the summation of each range value

and    k    = the number of samples taken

$$\overline{R} = \frac{7.6}{25} = 0.304 \tag{32}$$

Draw R or $\overline{R}$ bar on the range chart as a thick line.

Calculate the control limits for the range chart.

The control limits are used as a guide to determine process performance.  The use of the control limits is described in the section - STAGE 3 Data Analysis and Variation Reduction.

In order to calculate the control limits, it is necessary to use certain constants.  In the table - Control Limit Constants for each sample size n are given constants $A_2$, $D_3$ and $D_4$ which are used in the control limit calculations.

The first constant to be used is $D_4$ which can be found in Table - Control Limit Constants by locating on row 'n' the sample size and read off the value for $D_4$. Record the value of $D_4$.

Calculate Upper Control Limit for ranges.

where $UCL_R = D_4 \times \overline{R}$

In the example $UCL_R = 2.114 \times 0.304 = 0.642$

Draw $UCL_R$ on the range chart as a thick line.

Calculate the Lower Control Limit for ranges.

$$LCL_R = D_3 \times \overline{R}$$

$D_3$ is given in the table - Control Limit Constants and is found in a similar way to $D_4$.

**Table 14** - Control Limit Constants

| n | 2 | 3 | 4 | 5 | 6 | 7 | 8 | 9 | 10 |
|---|---|---|---|---|---|---|---|---|---|
| $A_2$ | 1.880 | 1.023 | 0.729 | 0.577 | 0.483 | 0.419 | 0.373 | 0.337 | 0.308 |
| $D_3$ | 0 | 0 | 0 | 0 | 0 | 0.076 | 0.136 | 0.184 | 0.223 |
| $D_4$ | 3.268 | 2.574 | 2.282 | 2.114 | 2.004 | 1.924 | 1.864 | 1.816 | 1.777 |

In the example $LCL_R = 0 \times 0.304 = 0$

# Statistical Process Control

Draw $LCL_R$ on the range chart as a thick line.

Calculate the process average.

$$Average\ \bar{\bar{x}}\ =\ \frac{\Sigma\ xi}{k} \tag{33}$$

Where $\Sigma xi$ = the summation of each individual sample average

$$In\ the\ example\ (Completed\ SQC\ Chart)\ \bar{\bar{x}}\ =\ \frac{259.62}{25}\ =\ 10.38 \tag{34}$$

Draw x bar on the average chart as a thick line

Calculate the control limit for average charts.

Determine the value for $A_2$, where $A_2$ is given in the table; it is found in a similar way to $D_4$.

Calculate Upper Control Limit for averages

$$UCL_x\ =\ \bar{\bar{x}}\ +\ (A_2\ \times\ \bar{R}) \tag{35}$$

*In the example (Completed SQC Chart) $UCL_x$ = 10.38 + (0.577 x 0.304)*

Draw UCL$_x$ on the average chart as a thick line

Calculate the Lower Control Limit for averages:

$$LCL_x = \bar{\bar{x}} + (A_2 \times \bar{R}) \tag{36}$$

*In the example (Completed SQC Chart) LCL$_x$ = 10.38 - (0.577 x 0.304)*

Draw LCL$_x$ on the average chart as a thick line.

## STAGE 3 Data analysis and variation reduction

One of the key purposes of using control charts is to improve quality by reducing variation. Consequently, techniques need to be employed which can help identify any sources of variation. One such method is to identify the presence of non-random effects and, if possible, eliminate them. Non-random effects can be recognised by applying the following tests when examining the charts.

**TEST 1**         **Any point outside the control limit**

**TEST 2**         **A series of seven points above or below the average**

**TEST 3**         **A trend of seven points in a consistent direction from the mean**

**TEST 4**         **Any other cyclic pattern**

Once a non-random effect has been identified, its source should be investigated to determine what action is necessary to (a) correct the non-conformity and (b) prevent it recurring. As an aid to trouble shooting when non-random variations occur, it is important to keep a log of any changes such as re-setting, change of shift, material or equipment changes.

## TEST 1

*Points outside the control limits.* The control limits have been calculated using the constants ($A_2$, $D_3$ and $D_4$). These constants are calculated so that there is only a one in 1000 chance of points lying outside the Control Limits. It is reasonable, therefore, to presume that a non-random effect has caused the change.

A point outside the control limit (either above or below) could indicate that:

○        The point has been wrongly plotted

○        The control limit has been incorrectly calculated or plotted o        The process has worsened or improved

o        The inspection standard has changed


## TEST 2


*A series of seven points above or below the average.* A change in the process average could indicate that the average has moved and stabilised at a new higher or lower level. A run of seven points above the average could indicate that, on the average chart, the accuracy or process average has worsened. On the average chart, - a run of seven points below the average could indicate that the accuracy or process average has improved.

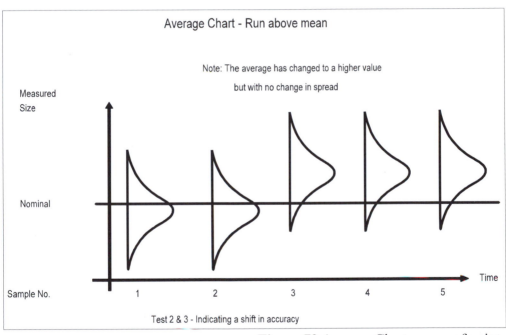

**Figure 73** Average Chart - a run of points

The effect on the process distribution is shown in **Figure 73**. The spread of the process has not changed but the setting has undergone a change, resulting in a shifted average and stabilising at a new higher level.

On the range chart - a run of seven points above the average would indicate the repeatability or spread of the process has worsened, or the inspection standard or measuring system has changed.

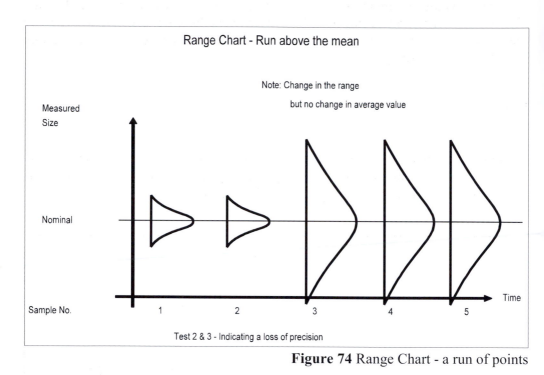

**Figure 74** Range Chart - a run of points

The effect on the process spread of a run of points above the average on the range chart is represented in **Figure 74**. The location of the spread has not changed but the width of the spread has increased. Consequently, there will be a greater variation between the individual process values.

**TEST 3**

Any trends within the control limits (even when all points are within the control limits) should be investigated as it may be an indication of conditions which, if ignored, could lead to the process moving outside the control limits, or an improvement opportunity that should be encouraged.

*Trends - on the average chart*

A run of seven points, where each point is higher or lower than the previous, may indicate that the accuracy or process average is changing and possibly worsening. The inspection standard or measuring system could be changing.

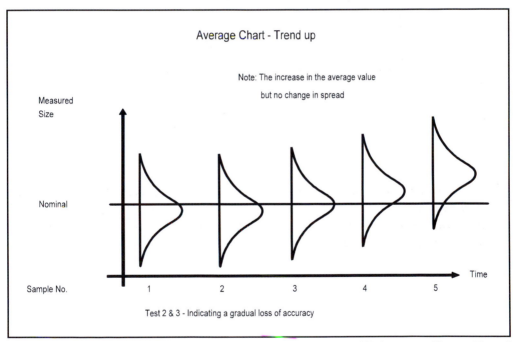

**Figure 75** Average Chart - Trend

**Figure 75** represents the effect on the process distribution as a result of a run of points on the average chart. There is no change in the process spread but a shift upwards of the process setting or location.

*Trends - on the Range Chart*

A run of seven points, where each point is higher than the previous could indicate that the repeatability or spread has worsened and is still deteriorating. A run of seven points, where each point is lower than the previous, could indicate that the repeatability or spread has improved and is still improving, so investigate and encourage this trend.

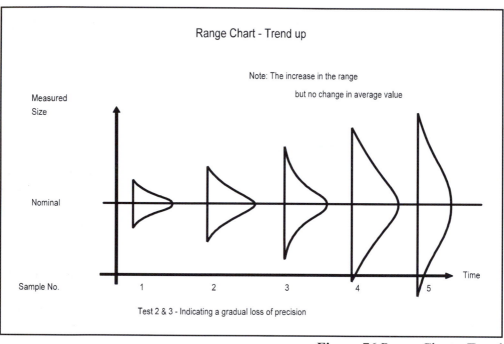

**Figure 76** Range Chart - Trend

**Figure 76** represents the changes to the process distribution as a consequence of a run upwards of points on the range chart. The spread of the distribution is deteriorating and there will be a steadily worsening variation between individual process values.

**TEST 4**

The control limits are such that approximately ⅔ of the data points should lie within the middle third region of the control limits. About ⅓ of the data points should lie in the outer two thirds region of the control limits.

Cyclic patterns may be due to plotting points from samples taken from different conditions e.g. different processes, different shifts, different batches.

**Variation reduction**

**Identification and remedy:** Once a non-random cause of variation has been investigated and remedied, the process should have improved. If subsequent data points are consistently below the previous average (confirming the improvement) then the control limits can be re-calculated for the new improved process performance.

**Continuous process improvement:** The data should continue to be collected, plotted on the chart and analysed to identify further process improvements. It may be appropriate to use the techniques associated with Total Quality Management to assist in achieving process improvements, particularly Pareto analysis and cause and effect diagrams.

## Attribute Charts and Data

The previous section described the procedure to be observed when SQC is applied to variable data. This section shows how to apply SQC when attribute data is collected.

The data will need to be divided into samples or sub-groups of 'n' items. The number of items in each sample should preferably remain constant (although this is not essential). The interval between each sample should be chosen on the basis of production frequency, the importance of the operation or process. The samples need to be sufficiently large to allow defectives to appear (although hopefully none). The samples should be taken from one process otherwise it will be difficult to identify the source or cause of any defectives. I.e. separate charts should be kept for different processes.

## STAGE 1  Gather the data

Decide on a sample size in accordance with the above rules.

Record the number of defects/defectives in each sample. See **Figure 77**.

A typical attribute SQC chart is shown next.

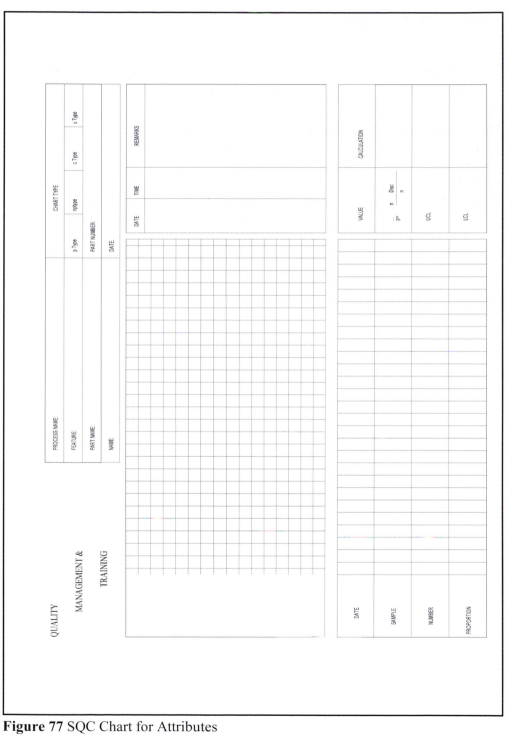

**Figure 77** SQC Chart for Attributes

# Statistical Process Control

The proportion or number of defects/defectives on the vertical axis and the sample identification (hour, day etc.) on the horizontal axis. The vertical axis should extend from zero to about 1.5 times the highest point expected.

Depending on the chart type selected, plot the value of p, np, c or u for each sample on the chart.

## STAGE 2  Determine the control limits

*(i)  The p chart for Proportion of Defectives (non-conforming units)*

The proportion of defectives is p i.e. the number of defectives (np) divided by the number in the sample.

$$p = \frac{np}{n} \tag{37}$$

Calculate the average number of defectives for the process.

$$\bar{p} = \frac{Total\ number\ defectives}{Total\ number\ inspected} \tag{38}$$

A typical completed SQC chart for attributes is shown next.

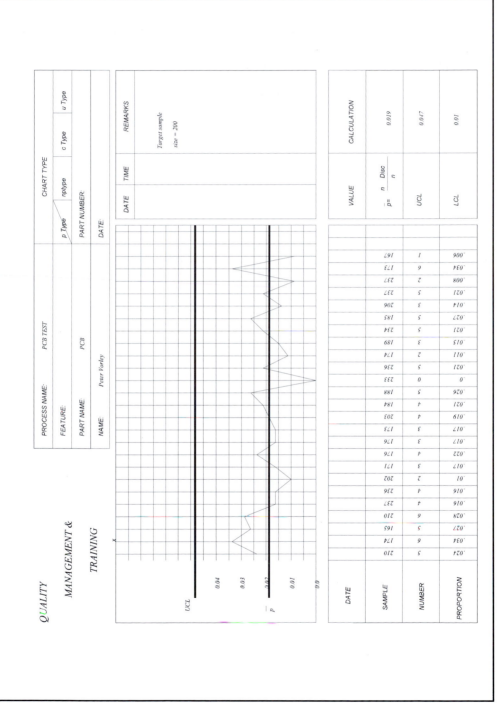

**Figure 78** Completed SQC Chart for Attributes

Calculate the Control Limits (UCL, LCL).

$$UCL_p = \bar{p} + 3 * \sqrt{\frac{\bar{p}(1-\bar{p})}{n}}$$ (39)

$$LCL_p = \bar{p} - 3 * \sqrt{\frac{\bar{p}(1-\bar{p})}{n}}$$ (40)

Draw the process mean (p bar) and control limits on the chart and label (p, UCL$_p$ and LCL$_p$).

**Note 1:**

As the sample size can vary with p charts then this can affect the control limits. Therefore, it may be necessary to recalculate the control limits. Once calculated the new control limits should be plotted on the control charts.

**Note 2:**

If the LCL is negative then ignore this control limit, since it is not possible to have less than zero defectives. (See **Figure 78** Completed SQC Chart for Attributes).

# Introduction to Quality

*ii) The np chart for number of Defectives*

The number of defectives is np i.e. the number in the sample multiplied by the proportion of defectives in the sample.

Calculate the average number of defectives for the process

$$\overline{np} = \frac{np_1 + np_2 + np_3 + \text{.....}np_n}{m} \tag{41}$$

Where $np_1$, $np_2$ etc. are the number of defectives in each of m samples inspected.

Calculate the Control Limits (UCL, LCL).

$$UCL_{np} = \overline{np} + 3 * \sqrt{\frac{\overline{np}(1-\overline{np})}{n}} \tag{42}$$

$$LCL_{np} = \overline{np} - 3 * \sqrt{\frac{\overline{np}(1-\overline{np})}{n}} \tag{43}$$

Draw the process mean and control limits on the chart and label (np, $UCL_{np}$ and $LCL_{np}$).

**Note:**

If the LCL is negative ignore this control limit, since it is not possible to have less than zero defectives.

# Statistical Process Control

*iii) The c chart for number of Defects (Non-conformities)*

The number of defects is c.

Calculate the average number of defects for the process

$$\bar{c} = \frac{c_1 + c_2 + c_3 + .....c_m}{m} \tag{44}$$

Where $c_1$, $c_2$ etc. are the number of defects in each of m samples inspected.

Calculate the Control Limits (UCL, LCL).

$$UCL_c = \bar{c} + 3*\sqrt{\bar{c}} \tag{45}$$

$$LCL_c = \bar{c} - (3*\sqrt{\bar{c}} \tag{46}$$

Draw the process mean and control limits on the chart and label (c, $UCL_c$ and $LCL_c$).

**Note:** If the LCL is negative ignore this control limit, since it is not possible to have less than zero defectives.

*iv) The u chart for number of Defects (Non-conformities) per Unit*

The number of defects per unit is u.

Calculate the average number of defects per unit for the process

$$\bar{u} = \frac{u_1 + u_2 + u_3 + \ldots u_m}{n_1 + n_2 + n_3 + \ldots n_m} \qquad (47)$$

Where $u_1$, $u_2$ etc. are the number of defects per unit in each of m samples inspected.

Calculate the Control Limits (UCL, LCL).

$$UCL_u = \bar{u} + 3 * \sqrt{\frac{\bar{u}}{n}} \qquad (48)$$

$$LCL_u = \bar{u} - 3 * \sqrt{\frac{\bar{u}}{n}} \qquad (49)$$

Draw the process mean and control limits on the chart and label (u, $UCL_u$ and $LCL_u$).

**Note 1:**

As the sample size can vary with u charts then this can affect the control limits. Therefore, it may be necessary to recalculate the control limits with each new sample size. Once calculated, the new control limits should be plotted on the control charts.

**Note 2:**

If the LCL is negative then ignore this control limit, since it is not possible to have less than zero defectives.

**Multiple characteristic charts**

With any of the above p, np, c and u charts, it is only possible to monitor one characteristic. With all of these charts (p, np, c, and u) it may on occasion be necessary to monitor more than one characteristic or feature. In this situation, a multiple characteristic chart can be employed which enables several characteristics to be recorded on the one chart. Thus giving a more comprehensive picture of the process performance and assisting with identifying the causes of variation. (See **Figure 79** Attribute Control Chart - Multiple Features). Note that a Pareto Analysis of the various characteristics can be performed on the data calculated on the right-hand side of the chart.

**Figure 79** Attribute Control Chart - Multiple Features

237

# Statistical Process Control

## Control chart exercise

*Questions*

1. Why is it not advisable to show the process specification or tolerance on the control charts for variables?

2. If the tolerance limits are to be shown on performance based variable charts how should they be shown?

3. What are the upper and lower control limits for variable and attribute charts based on and why is this method selected?

*Answers*

1. *Why is it not advisable to show the specification tolerance on the control charts for variables?*

Because the average value of the samples taken is plotted not the actual value. This has the effect of reducing variation or compressing the values by a factor of;

$$\frac{1}{\sqrt{n}}$$

Where n is the number in the sample.

The consequence of this would be that all values would appear to be within tolerance, when this may not be the case.

238

2.  *If the tolerance limits are to be shown on performance based variable charts how could they be shown?*

Either by using tolerance based control charts where the control limits are calculated by;

$$\text{Upper or Lower Control Limit } = \text{ Specification Limit } \pm 3 * \frac{\sigma}{\sqrt{n}}$$

Where $\sigma$ = The standard deviation of the process

$n$ = Sample size

$\sigma_n$ = Standard deviation of the average of the samples

Or by showing the tolerance as a *'corrected tolerance'* (based on the sample mean);

$$\frac{Tolerance}{\sqrt{n}}$$

on performance based control charts.

3.  *What are the upper and lower control limits for variable and attribute charts based on and why is this method selected?*

The mean ± 3 standard deviation, because there is approximately a 1 in 1000 chance of a value being outside these values, which indicates an improbable event.

Part 6

Reliability

# Introduction to Quality

## Reliability

## Basic Concepts

Reliability is fundamental to Quality. However, the level intended in this book is only an introduction to the subject.

*Reliability - A Definition*

Reliability is the *ability* of a component or system made up of many components, expressed by the *probability* that it will *perform* its required *function* under stated *conditions* for a stated period of *time*.

*Parameters* - which must be stated:

- Time - cycles, miles, hours?
- Conditions - environment?
- Function - what is failure?
- Ability - expressed as probability (maths field)

*Reliability your Best Investment:* The unreliability of British products is a topic which is often discussed, in much the same way as the wider aspects of the "British disease". Yet some companies have shown that application of modern reliability engineering methods, as pioneered in military and space projects, can be very good business, if not essential to a product's success. History is littered with examples of UNRELIABLE systems.

- 1879 Tay Bridge

  Use of inadequate materials, lack of knowledge of sub-soil.

- 1939/45 American Liberty Ships

  All welded structures, allowing cracks to propagate very rapidly, causing ship to break in half. Failure in a brittle mode. Such failure does not occur in rivetted ships, since any crack which begins to run will terminate at the first rivet hole.

# Reliability

○ 1953/54 Comets

Low level cyclic stresses caused by aircraft climbing and descending combined with pressurised interior. The final fatigue failure was due to stress concentration at the corner of square windows.

○ 1940 Tacoma Narrow Bridge

Span of 840m, was built without adequate torsional stiffness, subsequently it swayed, even in the most moderate breeze, wriggling itself into collapse in a high wind.

○ 1980 the Norwegian Oil Rig Collapse

Due to the cutting of a ledge on one of the feet to mount an instrument panel.

○ 1986 Chernobyl Disaster

Due to switching off the safety backup systems


The major reasons for the steady increase in reliability study in the last four decades have been:

○ Space research and development, where an unreliable component or system could lead to the write off of some very expensive equipment. There are no service stations on the moon!

○ The cost of ownership of a product or system is made up of three components:

  • *Capital*

  • *Operating, Administrating, Maintaining and Replacing* which could far exceed (1)

  • *Availability* - the cost of having a system out of commission for any length of time.

○ Military system requirements.

○ The market place economy and modern competitiveness.

# Introduction to Quality

Much of reliability research has been on electronic components and systems due to:

i.   greater population for test purposes,

ii.  more easily tested,

iii. longer, useful predictable life with electronic and electrical components. However, it is also possible to fit reliability theory to mechanical situations.


Reliability Engineering is the collection of test and field data of components and systems and its subsequent analysis after which it is possible to:

a.   State numerically the reliability of a system after a given period of time with the degree of confidence, e.g. a space satellite has a better than 99% probability of being operational after 10 years with a confidence of 90%.

b.   Use reliability data to compare and improve systems at the design feasibility study stage, e.g. to compare two satellite designs.

c.   Feed back field data into the design and production system to ensure greater future reliability of the product.

d.   Predict expected life and guarantee periods.

e.   Plan maintenance schedules from the analysis of reliability data.


Ultimately reliability depends upon:

o   Designers

o   Materials Engineers

o   Production Engineers

o   Quality Systems

o   The Workforce


Mistakes at any stage may lead to an unreliable product. The statistical studies of distributions and probability theory is essential in handling reliability problems - although some specialised maths may be necessary. Reliability data involves a range of different distributions. Areas under these distributions represent percentages of the population of items under test. For example, the mean life of a product, or the Mean Time Between Failures (MTBF), may be estimated as having a value between 10,000 and 12,000 hours with a confidence of 90%.

*Acceptable Reliability*

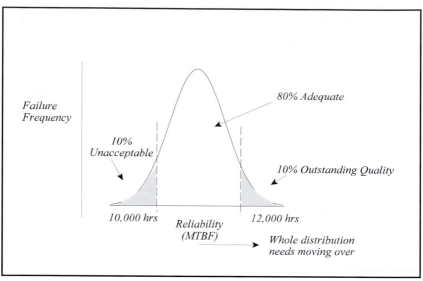

**Figure 80** Acceptable reliability

*Breakdown and Safety Margins*

Breakdown of components takes place when there is an overlap of breaking stress and working stress.

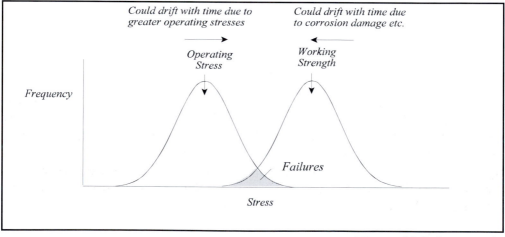

**Figure 81** Safety margin

Note in **Figure 81** the distribution to the right is the distribution of the strength of a batch of components. The distribution to the left is the distribution of stresses applied to the components during their active life. The two curves should not overlap, i.e. safety margins should be adequate. A component with low working strength and high operating stress would fracture.

In the next diagram, Breakdown and Safety Margins are shown decreasing, as the strength and load distributions drift together then the potential wear-out failure curve at the bottom right of the diagram is generated.

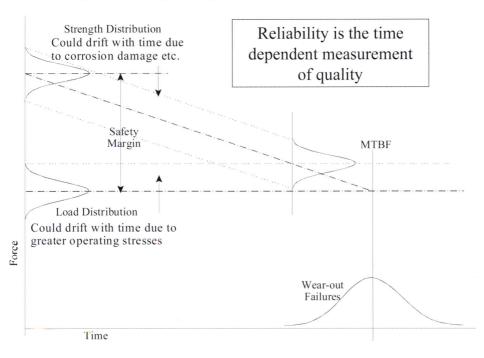

**Figure 82** Breakdown and Safety Margins

**Figure 82** is similar to **Figure 81** in that the upper distribution is the distribution of the strength of a batch of components. The lower distribution is the distribution of stresses applied to the components during their active life. The two curves should not overlap, i.e. safety margins should be adequate. A component with low working strength and high operating stress would fracture. In this **Figure 82**, the effect of the strength distribution drifting down on the Mean Time Between Failure (MTBF) is shown at the bottom of the diagram, with the 'Wear-out failure' curve.

# Reliability

## Patterns of Failure

*Failure* - the termination of the ability of a component or system to perform as required function.

Reliability is the time dependent measurement of quality. Products leaving the production line may be inspected for defects or deviations from specified requirements. However, there may be weaknesses which have not been determined by final inspection. In addition, weaknesses may have been introduced during packaging, despatch and installation. What is more, products deteriorate during use and eventually wear out. Thus reliability is quality in service.

From our everyday experience we have come to expect that the reliability of a new product improves over the first few months and settles down to a reasonable life expectancy before wear-out sets in when the reliability deteriorates. We need to understand these phases in more detail. First we shall look at them qualitatively then we shall look at the mathematical values.

*Early Failures*

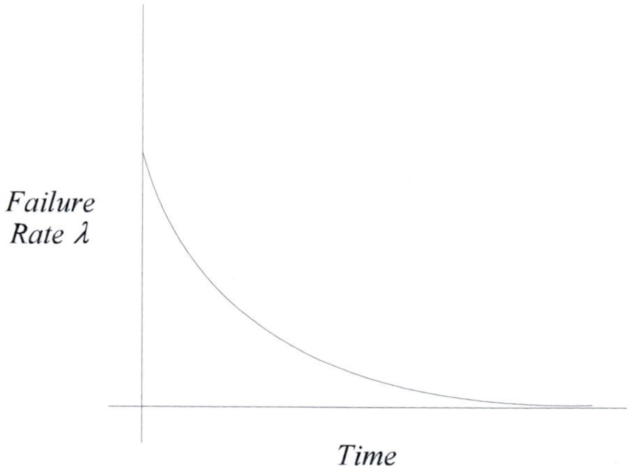

Early failures are those resulting from inherent weaknesses present in the as-made condition such as new components, which are untried, failing due to manufacturing faults, poor design, installation errors, misuse. Take for example, a multi-core cable which is stripped using wire strippers which have been set too tight, in stripping the cable some of the conductors are severed and removed.

*Failure Rate λ*

*Time*

**Figure 83** Distribution of early failure rate

Subsequently, the cable is soldered into position. The joint is tested for continuity and found to be acceptable. However, the result is a product or system with an inherent weakness which will

246

cause premature failure. The traditional approach to this is to allow a factor of safety in the design, however, the frontiers of technology have been eating into this indulgence in over design in order to save weight and increased miniaturisation. Such failures tend to be eliminated during the early life of the product and are therefore referred to as infant mortalities. This phase is also sometimes called the 'burn in' period. In safety critical situations it has been common practice to use soak tests and/or burn-in techniques to detect and remove defectives before release. This period is usually covered by guarantee.

*Random Cause Failures*

Once early failures are renewed and replaced the failure rate, although usually low, may be troublesome. The problem is that these failures are unlikely to be due to a simple single cause, i.e. they are randomised. (If failures are from a particular cause the failure is not random and will occur with a specific pattern and should therefore be fairly easy to diagnose).

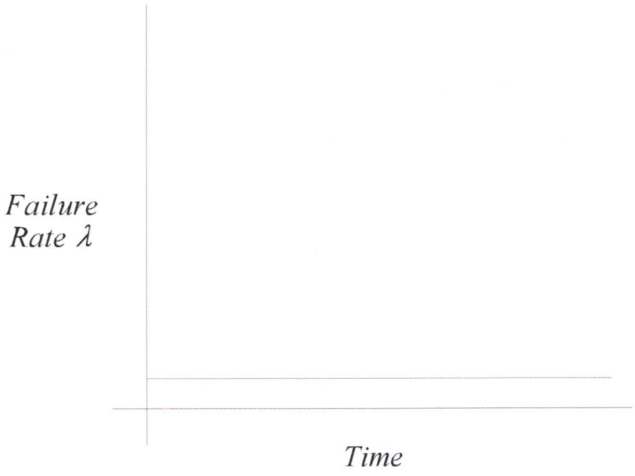

*Failure Rate λ*

*Time*

**Figure 84** Constant failure rate distribution

However, in addition to the early failures due to component weaknesses, failures may occur which cannot be assigned to any special cause. The failure pattern is purely random and occurs at a constant rate throughout the life of the product. Continuing with the human analogy, even after infant mortalities have occurred deaths still occur as a result of unpredictable causes. Acknowledging that these are unpredictable does not remove man's quest for refining his knowledge of these special causes. In such circumstances it is usual to make contingency plans and use design techniques such as:

o   De-rating        Using components at a lower rate than they are designed for, e.g. using resistors rated for 250 volt operation in a 25 volt application.

o   Redundancy      Using double or triple parallel systems, e.g. the provision two light sources in an overhead projector.

○ Fail-safe          Designing systems such that any failure results in a safe mode, e.g. if a thermostat in a washing machine fails it fails off and not on, i.e. the power to the heater is disconnected.

○ Fail-soft          Designing systems such that when they fail they do not cease to operate   suddenly, e.g. if a power supply fails a battery or generator cuts in to maintain continuity of power.

*Wear-out Failures*

The third failure process is due to wear out. Over a period of time everything wears out. Components wear, erode and weaken . Mating parts wear, increasing clearances. Dry cell batteries suffer chemical changes. Creep, fatigue, corrosion and erosion are all wearing factors to be considered. An estimate of the time to wear out for systems

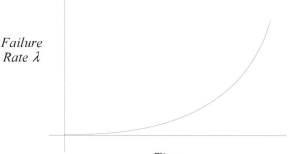

*Failure Rate λ*

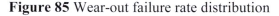

*Time*

**Figure 85** Wear-out failure rate distribution

and components would be useful. Fatigue has been the subject of much analysis and other techniques such as Weibull analysis provide information on likely time scales of potential failures.

During this period the failure rate increases. As components wear out the overall failure rate increases with time in maintained systems with components which are not subjected to maintenance, or which are un-maintainable. This model may be changed due to policy pursued e.g. frequency of inspection, the replacement of renewable parts. The model is typical of most electronics devices, although, mechanical systems and components may follow this characteristic.

*Complete Life Failure Patterns - the Bathtub Curve*

Combining these failures together produces a failure distribution commonly referred to as the bath-tub curve for obvious reasons. The bathtub curve is the classical pattern of failure against time and the mathematical model is a useful starting point from which to investigate practically.

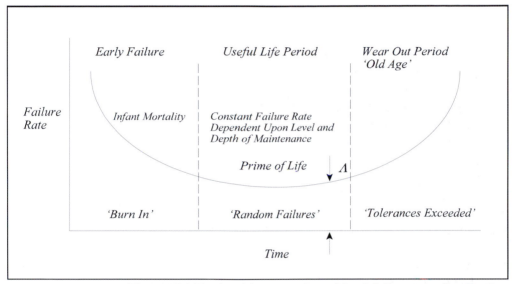

**Figure 86** 'Bath tub' curve of combined failure rate distribution

Notes: The above curve is for complex equipment restored to good-as-new on failure during useful life period. A large batch of components on test may have a similar characteristic. It should also be noted that random and wear out failures occur over the whole of the life cycle of a system.

*Reliability Calculations*

From all practical considerations, the period we are most interested in is the 'useful life' period. i.e. the constant failure rate period.

*Constant Failure Rate*

Although this is a period of constant failure rate, the reliability will fall exponentially. Consider 1000 components which fail at a constant rate of 10% per month. After one month there will be 100 failures leaving 900 components. After two months there will be 90 failures leaving 810 components. After three months there will be 81 failures leaving 729 components. In other words, the reliability after one month is 90%, after two months is 81% and after three months is 73%.

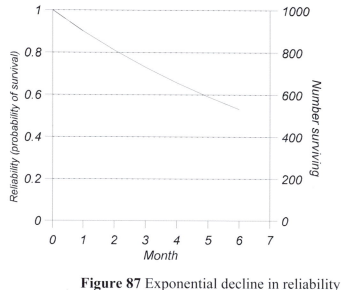

**Figure 87** Exponential decline in reliability

*Calculating the failure rate λ (LAMDA)*

The failure rate can be estimated from a test and is the number of failures divided by the total number of hours of survival for the period of the test.

Example 1       On a test of 1,000 components, 10 fail in 5,000 hours. Defective items are replaced. The test is truncated after 5,000 hours to exclude wear out failures.

$$\lambda \quad = \quad \frac{\text{failure}}{\text{component hours}} \quad = \quad \frac{10}{5,000 \times 1,000} \quad = \quad 2 \times 10^{-6}/\text{hr}$$

$$= \quad 2 \text{ components/million hours}$$

Note: Replacement tests are seldom used, as it involves constant observation to replace the defective item.

Example 2     A non-replacement test of 10 items is truncated after 1,000 hours. Three items failed at 300, 672 and 806 hours respectively. The remainder were still working at the end of the test.

$$\lambda \quad = \quad \frac{3}{300 + 672 + 806 + (7 \times 1,000)} \quad = \quad 0.000342/\text{hr}$$

$$= \quad 342/10^{-6} \text{ hrs}$$

*Calculating the Mean Time Between Failures (MTBF δ)*

The MTBF is the inverse of the failure rate, i.e. MTBF = 1/λ

Thus for example 1

$$\delta \quad = \quad \frac{1}{2 \times 10^{-6}} \quad = \quad 500,000 \text{ hrs}$$

and example 2

$$\delta \quad = \quad \frac{1}{342 \times 10^{-6}} \quad = \quad 2,924 \text{ hrs}$$

# Reliability

*Constant Failure Rate Curves*

Consider a number of components on test during the random failure period.

If $\lambda_t$ is the failure rate, over a period of time t the expectation of failures will be:

$$m = \lambda t$$

e.g. if $\lambda = 0.001/hr$, $t = 1,000$ hrs the expected failures $m = 0.001 \times 1,000 = 1$

The reliability during the constant failure rate period decays exponentially. Early in the 19$^{th}$ century a man named Poisson discovered a mathematical equation to define an exponential decay. The Poisson Distribution[17] can, therefore, be used to calculate the reliability at time *t*. This is the probability that there will be zero failures at time *t* and is given by the Poisson expression

$$R_t = e^{-\lambda t}$$

$$= \frac{1}{e^m} = \frac{1}{e^{\lambda t}} = e\text{-}\lambda t$$

It should be emphasised that in maintained systems, after the early failure period, the ages of the renewable component parts will have become randomised by previous failures. Under these circumstances, irrespective of the model for individual parts, for phase 2 of the system life, i.e. after the early failures rate phase, the system tends to have a nearly constant system failure rate.

The exponential distribution is the most widely used in life testing. This is because it is an appropriate model, in which failure of an item is not due to deterioration as a result of wear but rather to random events. This is a factor which must be monitored otherwise the wrong model may be used.

---

[17] See also Poisson Distribution on page 307

# Introduction to Quality

Probability of failure $F_t$ = the unreliability of a component or system = $1 - R_t$. $F_t$ is the summation of Poisson terms for 1, 2, 3, . . . . . infinity.

For a constant failure rate we can use the Poisson Distribution to calculate the probability of 0, 1, 2, 3, 4, .... etc. failures from a sample of n

Number of Defectives = 0　　1　　2　　3　　etc.

$$\text{Probability (p)} = \frac{1}{e^m} + \frac{m}{e^m} + \frac{m^2}{e^m 2!} + \frac{m^3}{e^m 3!} + ....etc.$$

where m = $\lambda_t$ and 2!, 3! means factorial 2, 3 etc.

$$1 = \frac{1}{e^m} + \frac{m}{e^m} + \frac{m^2}{e^m 2!} + \frac{m^3}{e^m 3!} + ....etc.$$

This means that eventually the probability is 1 that all units will fail.

## Conditions in Service

It must be remembered that all of the above is dependent on known conditions of use. In many circumstances these may be unknown or unpredictable. That is why it has been necessary to introduce legislation such as the M.O.T. test for vehicles more than three years of age in order to check safety critical features. Similarly, there is an increasing tendency to design-out do-it-yourself maintenance and servicing of commodities. For example, certain products cannot be bought but only leased so that the producer maintains control over the service and maintenance of their products.

# Reliability

## Reliability Prediction

In order to predict the reliability of a system it is necessary to know the reliability of its component parts. Hence reliability testing of components is necessary in order to supply the data required for the prediction of the reliability systems.

The MTBF can be obtained as we have already seen, but if further tests were made on identical components, i.e. using a new set of samples, the result would be different. Indeed a number of tests would yield a number of different MTBFs.

The true MTBF can only be obtained by allowing the entire batch to fail and evaluating the result.

The component manufacturer who adopts this technique will have very accurate data to offer, but alas have no product to sell.

In practice we are forced to test samples and to truncate our tests. Hence, only a small proportion of the population is tested. In any case, if a test were allowed to continue until all devices have failed, 20 to 30 years may be required for some electronic components.

It will be remembered that by sampling techniques, with respect to the Normal Distribution, we can state, using this model, the degree of confidence that the value sampled, e.g. IQ heights, weights, etc., would be valid.

Although MTBF in the constant failure rate mode does not exhibit a normal distribution, using mathematical techniques confidence limits may be established. For example, we may say that with a confidence of 90% that the MTBF for components will lie between 4,000 and 5,000 hours, when testing from given components samples.

# Introduction to Quality

## Introduction to Basic Probability Theory

To understand and be able to calculate system reliability a knowledge of probability theory is necessary.

Probabilities are generally related to a scale as follows:

| | | |
|---|---|---|
| 1.0 | - | You will die |
| 0.9 | - | |
| 0.8 | - | |
| | | First card dealt is not a heart |
| 0.7 | - | |
| 0.6 | - | |
| 0.5 | - | Tossed coin is heads |
| 0.4 | - | |
| 0.3 | - | |
| | | First card dealt is a heart |
| 0.2 | - | |
| 0.1 | - | |
| 0 | - | You will live forever |

Example 1

Probability of throwing a 4 with single die     $P = 1/6$

$= 0.166$

Example 2

Probability of cutting a king at cards     $P = 4/52$

(4 chances out of 52)     $= 0.07692$

# Reliability

Example 3

Probability of a 4 <u>or</u> a 6 with a single die

$$P = 1/6 + 1/6$$
$$= 2/6$$
$$= 0.3333$$

This is called the addition law and applies to OR events: i.e. if probability of event A is $P_A$ and probability of event B is $P_B$ then the probability of events A OR B is:

$$P_{A \text{ or } B} = P_A + P_B$$

Example 4

To calculate the probability of a 6 and a 6 with two dice.

All possible combinations may be represented as follows:

| | | | | | |
|---|---|---|---|---|---|
| 1 and 1 | 2 and 1 | 3 and 1 | 4 and 1 | 5 and 1 | 6 and 1 |
| 1 and 2 | 2 and 2 | 3 and 2 | 4 and 2 | 5 and 2 | 6 and 2 |
| 1 and 3 | 2 and 3 | 3 and 3 | 4 and 3 | 5 and 3 | 6 and 3 |
| 1 and 4 | 2 and 4 | 3 and 4 | 4 and 4 | 5 and 4 | 6 and 4 |
| 1 and 5 | 2 and 5 | 3 and 5 | 4 and 5 | 5 and 5 | 6 and 5 |
| 1 and 6 | 2 and 6 | 3 and 6 | 4 and 6 | 5 and 6 | 6 and 6 |

From this table it may be seen that there are 36 possible combinations but only one of them is a double six. Clearly one would not want to create a table every time it is necessary to know how to calculate the probabilities. Since the probability of the first die is 6 is 1/6 and the probability of the second die is 6 is 1/6 their respective probabilities are multiplied to obtain the combined probability.

Thus:

$$P = 1/6 \times 1/6$$
$$1/36$$
$$= 0.0277$$

## Introduction to Quality

This is called the multiplication law and applies to 'AND' events, i.e. if the probability of event A is $P_A$ and the probability of event B is $P_B$ then the probability of events A AND B is:

$$P_{A \text{ and } B} = P_A P_B = P_A \times P_B$$

The addition and multiplication laws can be combined, as follows:

Example 5

Probability of 7 with two dice

i.e.

(1 AND 6) OR (2 OR 5) OR (3 AND 4) OR (4 AND 3) OR (5 AND 2) OR (6 AND 1)

$(1/6 \times 1/6) + (1/6 \times 1/6) + (1/6 \times 1/6) + (1/6 \times 1/6) + (1/6 \times 1/6) + (1/6 \times 1/6)$

$$= \quad 1/36 + 1/36 + 1/36 + 1/36 + 1/36 + 1/36$$

$$= \quad 6/36$$

$$= \quad 0.1666$$

This can be applied to a quality application.

Example 6

Consider a batch of which 2% is defective and calculate:

    i.     The probability of selecting a defective item.

    ii.     The probability of selecting two defective items.

    iii.     The probability of a good item followed by a defective item.

# Reliability

i.     Probability of one defective $P_d$       $=$    $0.02$

ii.    Probability of two defectives $P_{2d}$      $=$    $P_d \times P_d$

                                                       $=$    $0.02 \times 0.02$

                                                       $=$    $0.0004$

iii.   Probability of a good and a defective $P_{g \text{ and } d}$   $=$    $P_g \times P_d$

                                                       $=$    $0.98 \times 0.02$

                                                       $=$    $0.0196$

Note: If order does not matter, i.e. a defective item followed by good item OR a good item followed by a defective item, then:

$P_{\text{good OR bad}}$        $=$       $(0.98 \times 0.02) + (0.02 \times 0.98)$

                              $=$         $2 \times 0.0196$

                              $=$         $0.0392$

## Example 7

If the chance of failing a batch of goods by sampling is 2%, calculate:

(1)    the chance of failing 5 consecutive batches.

(2)    the chance of passing 5 consecutive batches.

(3)    the chance of failing any two in three.

(1)    $P_{F5}$          $=$       $0.02 \times 0.02 \times 0.02 \times 0.02 \times 0.02$

                            $=$       $3.2 \times 10^{-9}$

                            $=$       $0.0000000032$

(2)    $P_{P5}$          $=$       $0.98^5$

                            $=$       $0.904$

(3)      $P_{FFP}$ = 0.02 x 0.02 x 0.98

= 0.000392

$P_{FPF}$ = 0.02 x 0.98 x 0.02

= 0.000392

$P_{PFF}$ = 0.98 x 0.02 x 0.02

= 0.000392

adding these three possible combinations we get:

= 0.001176

Example 8

What is the chance of a 100 component assembly working when each component has a 1% unreliability.

$P_{total} = P_{component\ 1} \times P_{component\ 2} \times P_{component\ 3} \times \ ........\ P_{component\ 100}$

$P_{total} = 0.99 \times 0.99 \times 0.99 \times\ ........\ 0.99$

$P_{total} = 0.99^{\ 100}$

$P_{total} = 0.366$ or 36% (not very much is it!)

See what happens if there are 1000 components.

## Serial and Parallel (Systems) Reliability

When two or more units are linked this is called a system. The links may be in series or parallel or a combination of series and parallel. The reliability of the system depends on the type of link. A series system is an example of 'AND' events in that all units in series must be operable for system success. A parallel system is an example of 'OR' events in that the system will succeed if one or more units are operable.

*Series systems*

Consider a system of a given number of units or parts having reliability R1, R2, R3, etc. These may be represented in block form.

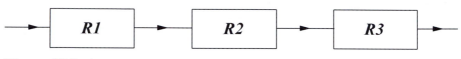

**Figure 88** Series system

If one component fails, the whole system fails, i.e. we have a series situation such as a chain where if one link fails the whole chain fails. Say R1 = R2 = R3 = 0.9 (probability of success) at a given time. What is the reliability of the system?

$$
\begin{aligned}
\text{Rs} \quad &= \quad \text{R1 x R2 x R3} \\
&= \quad 0.9 \text{ x } 0.9 \text{ x } 0.9 \\
&= \quad 0.73
\end{aligned}
$$

This is the probability of all devices working at the same time, which is an AND event.

*Parallel Systems*

In this situation, if any of the sub-systems operate then the system will work. This is more complex than it might at first appear. The simplest approach is to calculate the probability of failure of all sub-systems and subtract from 1. Consider a system of three sub-systems or parts operating in parallel, having reliability R1, R2, R3 respectively. These may be represented in block form as in **Figure 89**

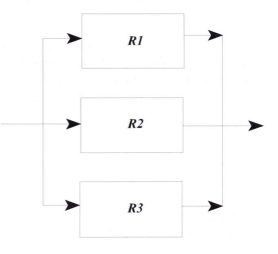

**Figure 89** Parallel system

The probability of success of the system is derived, as follows:

Probability of all sub-systems failing is

$$P_{1 \text{ and } 2 \text{ and } 3} = P_1 \text{ x } P_2 \text{ x } P_3$$
$$= (1 - R1) \text{ x } (1 - R2) \text{ x } (1 - R3)$$

Therefore, reliability is

$$R_{system} = 1 - ((1 - R1) \text{ x } (1 - R2) \text{ x } (1 - R3))$$

Let us assume that the respective reliabilities are 0.9 each.

$$
\begin{aligned}
Rs \quad &= \quad 1 - ((1 - 0.9) \text{ x } (1 - 0.9) \text{ x } (1 - 0.9)) \\
&= \quad 1 - (0.1 \text{ x } 0.1 \text{ x } 0.1) \\
&= \quad 1 - (0.001) \\
&= \quad 0.999
\end{aligned}
$$

# Reliability

This is a very important principle as it explains why cars have dual braking systems or aircraft have triple navigation systems. The provision of parallel systems to improve reliability is called **redundancy**.

## Reliability Improvement

When the reliability of the system has been established, it may be that the customer is not satisfied and so ways must be found of improving reliability.

The following are ways by which improvement may be achieved:

- by using components of superior quality.

- by de-rating the components and operating it at lower level than it is capable, i.e. improving the safety factors.

- by simplifying the design and making maintenance and repair easy and quick.

- by using '*burn in*' techniques to eliminate all defective units.

- by improving design, materials technology and production techniques.

- by using redundancy techniques, e.g. in space systems there may be up to five or six back up units, so that when one unit fails, another takes its place immediately; the three altimeters used in aircraft. This technique also enables systems to operate during repair and maintenance.

**Total Life Cycle Costing**

The costs of achieving a given reliability must be balanced against the cost of failure. There may well be many costs in failure including:

     a.       Damage to health and other property.

     b.       The costs due to unavailability of the product.

     c.       The excessive costs of repair. As in all things, a compromise is necessary as indicated in the following graph.

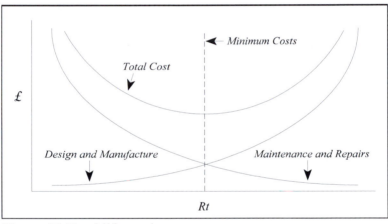

**Figure 90** Total life costing

**Practical Testing - burn-in phase**

In order to obtain constant failure rates of components, tests would be run, which is 'burning in' the batch and only components which survive the initial burning period would be analysed.

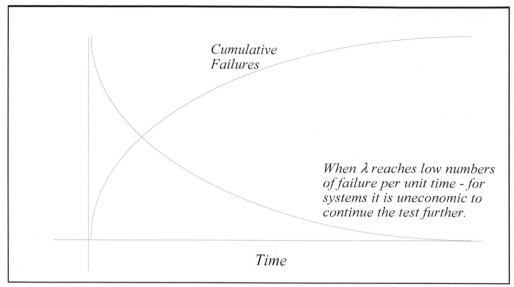

**Figure 91** Testing during burn-in phase

The times to failure are crucial to testing and these may be monitored by timing devices.

However, defining failure is not always straightforward, e.g. the square root key on a calculator may not be working. As this key will normally only be used intermittently, it would, under normal circumstances, take a long time to discover that fact.

Testing facilities should include monitoring of the complete system. Some systems, in fact, have an 'intelligence unit' which monitors its own system.

Field tests and monitoring are important, providing information is accurate and fed back to the manufacturers. A good example might be a service engineer carrying out repair work on 'white goods' such as washing machines and dishwashers. He will normally log the defective parts and after a period, the company will have a great deal of information concerning the reliability of its systems and components which make up those systems.

**Reliability Testing**

*General Considerations*

Tests tend to be both expensive and difficult, thus they should not be started without full consideration of their probable cost, balanced against the value of the information hoped to be obtained from them. The magnitude of the problem may be judged by considering typical failure rates, e.g. a failure rate might be of the order of 0.01 per cent per 1,000 hours, which means that on average the part will operate for 10,000,000 hours before a failure occurs. Now 10,000,000 hours is approximately 59,524 weeks or 1,145 years, assuming that testing continues 24 hours a day and seven days a week for 365 days a year! Clearly this is impossible, but the time can, of course, be reduced by testing a group of parts together. Thus if 1,000 parts are tested concurrently then 10,000,000 hours can be accumulated in a mere 1.145 years! But even during this time only one failure would be expected. A considerably longer testing time, or number of parts under test, would be necessary for there to be a significant number of failures. However, in many practical cases, the time available for testing is limited by the terms of the contract. If a complete system has to be designed, made and installed in, say, three years, the fraction of this available for development testing and generally proving the design will be measured in months at the most and probably only in weeks.

A further limitation will be the availability of test rigs. If 1,000 parts are to be put on test, in effect the test rig must provide 1,000 independent tests. Allowing for the fact that a number of such tests are likely to be running at the same time, it can be seen that the cost of all the test rigs may be very high and that even then there will only be a limited capacity available. Too often, in practice, the design of a given test is decided more by what is *possible* rather than by what *ought* to be done.

Thus the sequence might be:

1. The number to be tested is set by the number of places available on the test rig.

2. The duration of the test is decided by the time available before the results must be ready.

3. In such circumstances the reliability engineer may be able to do no more than calculate the confidence, or lack of confidence, which can be placed on the results.

# Reliability

*Types of Test*

Most reliability tests can be divided into one of two groups.

1.  *Reliability Demonstration and Acceptance Tests*

    In these tests the objective is usually to show that the reliability of certain items is at least equal to and, therefore, probably better than some pre-set value. It may not be necessary to determine the precise value of their reliability. Thus a manufacturer, having produced certain equipment, may wish to demonstrate to a customer that its reliability is at least as good as it is claimed to be. He therefore performs what he will call a *reliability demonstration test*. On the other hand, if the customer receives the equipment untested and then decides to do the tests himself, he will consider that he is doing a *reliability acceptance test*. To verify that the equipment satisfies the values for reliability given in the specification. Hence, reliability acceptance tests and demonstration tests are fundamentally the same, but done from a different perspective.

2.  *Reliability Measurements*

    If mere demonstration is insufficient, then tests can be devised to estimate some quantitative parameter. This might be the reliability directly but in many cases will be the failure rate or mean time between failures (MTBF). In addition to reliability, tests can be devised to check almost any aspect. For example:

    a.  *Maintainability*

        This is the relative speed with which the same repair can be carried out on two alternative designs. If the precise method for doing a repair is known, the time it will take may be estimated without anyone actually doing the job.

    b.  *Operability*

        This is the frequency of operator mistakes or the time required to do a job.

# Introduction to Quality

c.  *Product Quality*

This is the field of quality control as opposed to reliability testing but there is no sharp dividing line between the two. Better quality control results in subsequent reliability.

The type of test listed immediately above can often be carried out in a relatively short time and, therefore, might be preferred to a full reliability type test if the required information could be obtained from it.

*Testing components, sub-systems or complete systems*

The implications, so far, are that tests will be made on individual parts, such as resistors, capacitors or maybe mechanical linkages. Clearly this need not be so, and anything can be tested. However, difficulties and costs multiply with scale. If 1,000 components are expensive to test, 1,000 sub-systems will be even more so and in general, a test on 1,000 complete systems will not be practicable unless they are very small. Often the only real test on a complete system is that carried out by the customer in the course of normal operation. Even the manufacturer may only do it by parts.

*Accelerated Tests*

One way to reduce the very long test times which are often necessary is to use an accelerated test. The idea is that the normal life cycle of the item concerned should be compressed into a much shorter time. It takes two main forms.

1.  Tests done under normal use conditions (which would in practice be intermittent use) become either continuous use or something approaching it. Consider, for example, the ordinary cheap camera which people buy for their holiday photographs. The manufacturer wishing to life test these might argue that the average number of photographs taken per year seldom exceeds, say, 100 and most people expect, say,10 years use. Hence the acceptable life of such a camera is about 1,000 photographs. Now the shutter mechanism of a camera can easily be given 1,000 operations in the course of an hour or so and after that it can be run on until it fails just to find out how long it will last. Hence a life test to destruction, representing more than 10 years of life, can be completed in a few hours.

# Reliability

A somewhat similar test can be devised to test the wearing properties of a carpet. A sample of the carpet might be installed in the foyer of a theatre or even in a railway station. The number of people walking on it would vastly exceed what it would get in a home and so its wearing qualities would be quickly determined. Furthermore, the number of tickets issued by the theatre or railway station would give an estimate of the number of people who had walked on it.

In both of the above examples, although the life of the article is compressed into a short time, the conditions of use are approximately normal and the results will probably be reasonably reliable.

2.    Tests where the normal conditions of use are intensified.

Suppose it is required to test a batch of resistors or capacitors. Calculations along the lines discussed show that under normal conditions the test will take years to complete. It is, therefore, decided to increase the failure rate artificially by increasing both the test voltage and the ambient temperature. In this way it can be argued that potential failures can be detected in a few weeks instead of years. Unfortunately, however, this type of test must be approached with considerable caution.

*Environmental Tests*

In general there is little value in knowing whether an item will work satisfactorily in a clean, vibration and shock free, temperature controlled laboratory. Reliability under normal working conditions is more relevant. Therefore, many life tests will be done under simulated environmental conditions. They can, of course, be done in the actual working environment and nothing could be better than the real thing. Thus painted samples are sometimes left out in the open, exposed to the weather for months, so that their deterioration can be observed. Control of such a test is difficult. However, for example, if two pieces of equipment are each exposed to tropical storms and A fails while B survives, the failure may be because A was inferior or because it was exposed to much fiercer storms.

Hence reliability engineers normally install in their test laboratories equipment which will simulate the various environments in which they are interested under controlled conditions. The test conditions are then precisely known and the reliability of different types of equipment can be validly compared. Thus typical test equipment will include ovens which can apply various combinations of temperature and humidity, refrigeration plant and equipment to apply various combinations of vibration, bump, shock, etc. There still remains, of course, the vital problem of matching the conditions applied in the laboratory with those found in practice.

## Prototype Testing

At the prototype or pilot-production stage 1, a few, or a pilot production run, depending on the complexity of the item, of the product will be built. These are not for sale but for assessment of the product and the processes that will be used to produce it. Before the design is finalised and approved for production, data gained from the prototypes must be used to verify that the product will conform to its safety standards.

An important aspect of prototype testing is field trials. Testing against the relevant standards and specifications is effective but limited to the features they cover. These may not be as complete as expected, and testing in live conditions is a valuable further check. However, the tests must be chosen carefully to reflect the full range of conditions in which the final product will be used. Effective testing also means the close involvement of the purchaser, the end-users and other 'stakeholders' in defining, preparing, executing and evaluating the tests. Incidentally, when field trials have been completed, it is important to make sure that the test environment is restored to its pre-trial state.

When the prototype is proved to be fit for production, the design is frozen and placed under 'configuration control'. Production for sale can then commence. Thereafter, the product will typically be tested before release and its overall performance reappraised periodically by more detailed tests on a sample.

Any further changes in the process or product specification which seem desirable in the light of production experience may only be introduced under the discipline of a formal engineering change procedure. These disciplines will continue to safeguard the safety provisions as well as all other aspects of product quality.

## Configuration Control

The commonly used expression 'configuration control', 'modification control', or 'baseline control', implies control of design details whether recorded on paper or on magnetic media. Configuration is defined as: 'The complete description of the product and the relationship of its constituent elements'. A particular approved configuration at a specific point in time acts as a 'configuration baseline'.

'Configuration control' is:

> The discipline that ensures that any proposed change, addition, modification or amendment to the configuration baseline shall be prepared, accepted and controlled in accordance with set procedures.

## Reliability Programme Management

Rather than designing and producing a product and then discovering how reliable it is in use, it is possible to specify an agreed reliability target and devise a programme to achieve it. It is essential that reliability be considered as a characteristic feature of a system, equipment or item from the beginning of its existence as a design concept to the end of its working life. This requires that each factor which affects reliability at any stage in the life of an item be identified and considered in its relationship to other factors. This procedure can be formalised into a reliability programme.

A reliability programme ought to provide for the preliminary and continuing study of both quantitative and qualitative requirements throughout all phases of a project, the updating of reliability assessments, the validation of specified requirements, and the integration of reliability activities with other elements of the development and operation programme. The phases are:

- Definition,
- Design,
- Development,
- Production,
- Operation.

### *Definition Phase*

This is the study of reliability requirements during which the function(s) of the product in relation to the operating and non-operating conditions including packaging, storage and transport are identified. This results in a statement of objectives that establishes targets which provide a basis for the design, development and demonstration of reliability achievement.

FOUR elements must be addressed for a meaningful definition of reliability:

1. Ability - the measure used for the reliability, e.g. probability of survival.
2. Performance - the measure of success, e.g. function.
3. Conditions - the conditions the item is designed to function under.
4. Time - the life expectancy associated with '1.' above.

The following table is presented as a guide for completing the definition phase.

| Ability - probability of success | Performance | | Conditions - what use/abuse and environment the product will be subject to during its useful life | Expected Life |
|---|---|---|---|---|
| | Must do | Must not do | | |
| | | | | |

**Figure 92** Reliability Definition

*Design and Development Phase*

During this phase, consideration should be given to the relative contributions of materials and component parts. Various techniques are available such as design reviews, FMECA[18] and FTA[19] studies, redundancy analysis, stress and worst case analysis, parts and sub-assembly testing, prototype performance testing, environmental testing, accelerated testing, reliability demonstration (testing to failure) etc.

*Production Phase*

Consideration needs to be given to the effect of process failures on reliability. Neglect or error during production may not be identified by inspection and testing. Studies need to be carried out to identify critical process controls that must be monitored to prevent field failures. Techniques available at this stage range from detailed work instructions and workmanship criteria to the application of FMECA for processes and Quality Planning.

---

[18] Failure Mode, Effect and Criticality Analysis

[19] Fault Tree Analysis

# Introduction to Quality

The arrangements for production testing designed to demonstrate continued reliability achievement must be defined. Screening techniques include run-in or burn-in of components and assemblies to filter out weaknesses in the product prior to release and to demonstrate reliability achievement. Information gained at this stage can provide invaluable feedback to the design and/or production stages to further prevent recurrence of early failures.

## Functional and Maintenance Phase

Even though the operation phase of the product is out of the hands of the producer and reliability is affected by the user, this may still be considered as an extension of the testing period. Therefore, data collection and analysis should be continued and followed up with design improvements. The warranty period provides vital feedback information for the producer.

Planned Preventive Maintenance (PPM) is essential if the predicted reliability is to be achieved. The reliability targets established at the definition phase will have included assumptions about servicing and maintenance. The expected reliability will only have meaning if these servicing and maintenance conditions continue to be applied during the useful life of the product.

# Part 7

# Variability

**Variability**

**Discrete and Continuous Variables**

Discrete variables are values varying in discrete or whole steps. In many situations the variables may vary on a continuous scale. For example, if the feet of 50 people were measured a metric scale might be used and depending on the precision of the measuring instrument, 50 different measurements would result. The probability distribution would therefore appear to be rectangular (one for each size). In the days

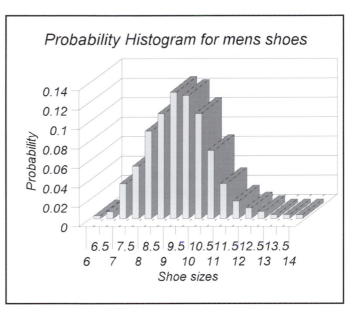

**Figure 93** Probability histogram for men's shoes

of craftsmen the shoemaker might make every pair of shoes to fit the individual and thus no two pairs of shoes would be identical. In these days of mass production it has been found that using discrete steps of ½ sizes of shoes is sufficient to satisfy the majority of people. Thus it would be useful to the shoemaker to have some idea of the probability distribution of the sizes of men's feet in relation to a scale of discrete steps of half sizes. The resulting probability distribution might be something like **Figure 93.**

Therefore, in order to have any distribution at all it is necessary to choose a suitable step when measuring a continuous variable. This step is called the **class interval**. In the absence of a natural class interval, as in the case of shoe sizes, it is usual to create a class interval based on the likely spread of the distribution divided into approximately 10 intervals.

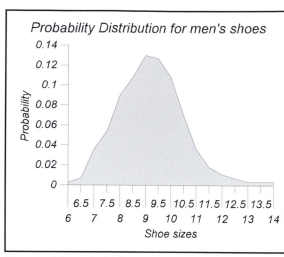

**Figure 94** Probability distribution curve

Another refinement of the probability distribution is to create a smooth envelope or probability distribution curve.

## Probability Distribution Patterns

As seen above, probability distribution patterns can take various shapes. Typical examples found in different circumstances are presented in the next diagrams:

276

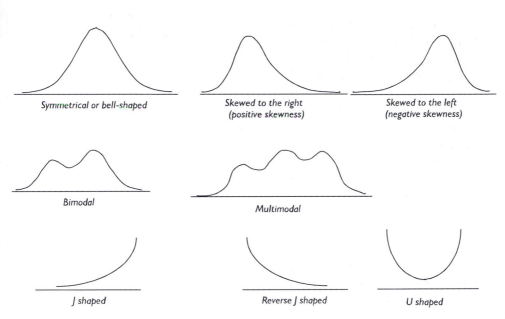

**Figure 95** Probability distributions

The distribution pattern of most interest in Statistical Quality Control is the symmetrical bell-shaped curve. The reason being that the variation of most stable processes will display such a distribution or something approximating to it. Try cutting a length of string into approximately 100 mm length by estimating and without measuring. Then construct a histogram and hence a frequency curve by smoothly joining the tops of the bars in the histogram. Cut 50 lengths then measure them accurately to the nearest mm. Do not be surprised if the curve looks something like the symmetrical bell-shaped curve.

As this curve is so central to Statistical Quality Control, it is important to explore its properties.

# Variability

## The Normal, Binomial and Poisson Distributions

## The Normal Distribution

The bell shaped curve referred to is called the Normal Distribution.

There are four variables to the bell shaped distribution:

1. The position of the curve on a scale.

2. The spread of the distribution.

3. The skewness of the distribution.

4. The peakedness of the distribution referred to as the Kurtosis.

For current purposes, discussion will be limited to the first two measures considering only a symmetrical bell-shaped curve.

## *Statistics of the Normal Distribution*

### 1. Position

It is quite common to talk of average values. However, there are different types of averages. At this stage three will be considered; the mode, the median and arithmetic mean.

   i. The Mode

   This is the value occurring with the most frequency. It is the value corresponding to the peak of the curve.

   ii. The Median

   This is the mid value or the value that divides the distribution into two equal halves.

iii.     The Arithmetic Mean

This is the sum of the values divided by the total number of values:

$$Mean = \frac{\Sigma \ of \ values}{n} \qquad\qquad (50)$$

Note: for a Normal Distribution, the values of the Mode, Median and Mean are the same.

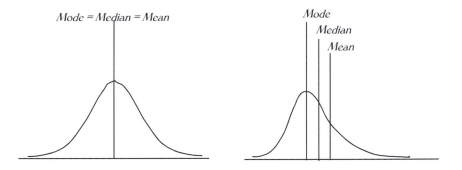

**Figure 96** Normal and skewed distributions

The Arithmetic Mean is the most common measure of distribution position.

**2.      Spread**

The mean value does not give complete information about a population (the variable).

Consider these two samples:

Sample No 1     Bar lengths     24, 23, 26, 27 units $\overline{X} = 25$

Sample No 2     Bar lengths      6, 37, 34, 23 units $\overline{X} = 25$

## Variability

Although in both samples the means are the same, the spreads are clearly different. Therefore, a suitable measure for spread is needed.

As with the position, a number of measures are available.

i.    The Range

The range is defined as the difference between the smallest and the greatest values. On the face of it this appears to be the best measure. However, it is difficult to be precise since the probabilities at the extremes get smaller and smaller but are not zero, so just where does the distribution start and finish?

ii.    The Mean Deviation

The deviations from the centre position could be averaged. However, this would mean ignoring the signs otherwise they would cancel each other out. Because of this, the value has no mathematical meaning.

iii.    The Variance

By squaring the deviations, the difficulty of the signs is overcome, since they all become positive when squared. If, the arithmetic mean of the squares of the deviations is calculated, then the result is what is called the variance, thus:

$$Variance = \frac{\Sigma \, deviations^2}{n} \qquad \textbf{(51)}$$

$$Variance = \frac{\Sigma f(x - \bar{x})^2}{\Sigma f} \qquad \textbf{(52)}$$

# Introduction to Quality

iv.    The Standard Deviation σ

The problem with the variance is that it is in square units. This means that while it has mathematical meaning it has no physical position on the curve. If the square root of the variance is taken, then we are back to linear units which does have a physical relationship to the distribution.

$$\sigma = \sqrt{\frac{\Sigma \, deviations^2}{n}} \qquad (53)$$

$$\sigma = \sqrt{\frac{\Sigma f(x - \bar{x})^2}{\Sigma f}} \qquad (54)$$

Sigma σ is the most common measure of spread of the distribution and can be readily calculated using a scientific calculator. The following method can also be used to calculate σ.

Example

| x | Coded value | f | fx | $(x - \bar{X})$ | $(x - \bar{X})^2$ | $f(x - \bar{X})^2$ |
|---|---|---|---|---|---|---|
| 100.1 | 0.1 | 3 | 0.3 | - 0.2033 | 0.0413 | 0.1239 |
| 100.2 | 0.2 | 7 | 1.4 | - 0.1033 | 0.0107 | 0.0749 |
| 100.3 | 0.3 | 10 | 3.0 | - 0.0033 | 0.00001 | 0.0001 |
| 100.4 | 0.4 | 6 | 2.4 | + 0.0967 | 0.0094 | 0.0564 |
| 100.5 | 0.5 | 4 | 2.0 | + 0.1967 | 0.0387 | 0.1548 |
|  |  | 30 | 9.1 |  |  | 0.4101 |

Notice coded values have been used for x to keep the numbers more manageable, i.e deviations from an arbitrary base line. The base line figure is then added to the mean, calculated using the coded values.

# Variability

$$\bar{x} = \frac{\sum fx}{\sum f} = \frac{9.1}{30} = 0.3033 \quad \therefore \ actual \ \bar{x} = 100.3033$$

$$\sigma = \sqrt{\frac{\sum f(x - \bar{x})^2}{\sum f}}$$

$$\sigma = \sqrt{\frac{0.4101}{30}} = 0.117$$

*Properties of the Normal Distribution*

Normal Distribution and Confidence Level - One of the main attractions of the normal distribution is the predictability of the percentages of values within given limits.

x is a variable

μ is the mean of the population.

σ is the standard deviation of the population

f (the vertical scale) is the frequency of the variable (the horizontal scale)

The area under the curve between specific values of x represents the percentage of the population within those values.

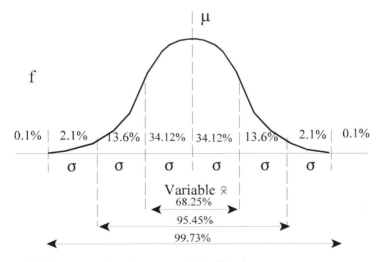

**Figure 97** Areas under the normal distribution

## The Normal Deviate

It can be seen from the above that the areas under the curve are relative to the standard deviation and the mean regardless of the scale of measurement used. An important statistic , therefore, when calculating probabilities based on the normal distribution is the distance between the mean and a specified value in units of standard deviations.

# Variability

$$\text{Normal deviate } u = \frac{(x - \mu)}{\sigma} \qquad (58)$$

**Example 1** If the mean height of the male population is 5 feet 10 inches. Then, assuming that the distribution is a normal distribution, i.e. symmetrical[20], there is a 50% probability that a male person picked at random, will have a height of 5 feet 10 inches or more.

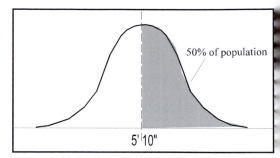

**Figure 98** Probability when u = 0

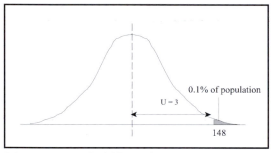

**Figure 99** Probability when u = 3

**Example 2** Suppose the distribution of IQs has a mean 100 and $\sigma = 16$. A person picked at random has an IQ of over 148 with a confidence of 99.9%

$$u = \frac{(148 - 100)}{16}$$

**Example 3** A person picked at random has an IQ between 84 and 115 with a confidence of 68%.

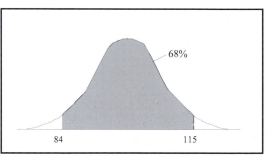

**Figure 100** Probability between limits

---

[20]      The examples shown are for illustration only. Real life distributions may vary from those shown here.

284

Whatever the distribution, providing the parameters follow specific equations, the area between given limits, may be found by integration. The area represents a level of confidence. A good example in reliability would be the Mean Time Between Failures (MTBF) factor, where a stated quantity might be that there is a 90% confidence of the MTBF being between 12,000 hours and 14,000 hours.

Consider some practical exercises involving the normal distribution, and areas between and outside specified limits.

**Example 4** Determine the percentage of product outside the specification limit

Specification limits: 100 $= \pm 2$ units

Process capability: $\overline{\text{X}}$ $= 100$ $\sigma = 0.75$

To find the area under the curve, first calculate the statistic u which is the number of standard deviations between the mean and a value x. (This is referred to as the normal deviate)

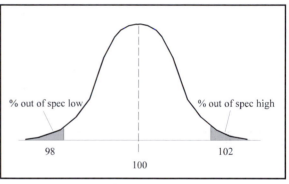

**Figure 101** Example 4

$$u = \frac{(x - \mu)}{\sigma}$$

$$= \frac{(102 - 100)}{0.75}$$

$$= 2.67$$

Referring now to Table 'Areas in Tail of the Normal Distribution' in *Murdoch and Barnes Statistical Tables*, this value of u corresponds to an area under the tail of 0.00379 (0.379%). In other words 0.379% of the work is likely to be oversize.

# Variability

Similarly for the lower limit:

The fact that u is negative is not important, the tables are still used in the same way. Thus 0.379% of the work will be undersize. This means that a total of 0.758% of the work will be outside the specified limits.

$$u = \frac{(x - \mu)}{\sigma}$$
$$= \frac{(98 - 100)}{0.75}$$
$$= -2.67$$

## Example 5

Specification limits: 100  $= \pm 3$ units

Process Capability: $\overline{X}$  $= 101$  $\sigma = 1.5$

For the upper limit:

$$u = \frac{(x - \mu)}{\sigma}$$
$$= \frac{(103 - 101)}{1.5}$$
$$= -1.33$$

Which corresponds to an area of 0.0918 or 9.18%.

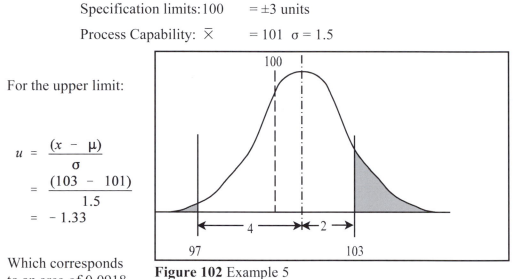

**Figure 102** Example 5

For the lower limit:

$$u = \frac{(x - \mu)}{\sigma}$$
$$= \frac{(97 - 101)}{1.5}$$
$$= -2.67$$

Which corresponds to an area of 0.00379 or 0.379% giving a total of 9.559% out of specification.

## Probability Paper

The following describes a tool that is used to determine if a distribution is normal and to estimate its parameters x and σ. First let us study the normal distribution in a little more detail. The area under the normal distribution varies from 0 to 1 (total area) as the intersection point moves from one extreme to the other thus:

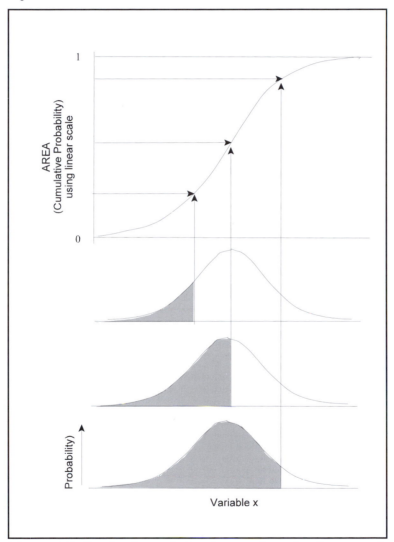

**Figure 103** Graph of cumulative frequencies using linear graph paper

# Variability

Now if the vertical scale could be stretched at each end and compressed in the centre by just the right amounts the curve could become a straight line thus:

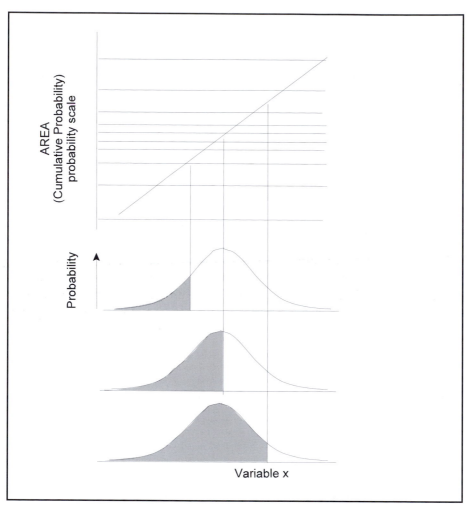

**Figure 104** Graph of cumulative frequencies using normal probability paper

Such graph paper does exist. It is called probability graph paper. Its significance is that only a Normal Distribution will form a straight line. Anything other than a straight line indicates a non-normal distribution.

288

Examples would be:

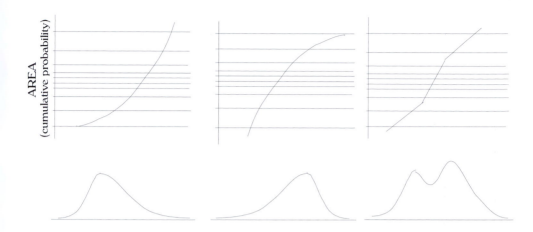

**Figure 105** Non-normal distributions on linear probability paper

Probability paper is also available for use when the distribution is skewed, e.g. 0 limited distribution. In such cases the linear horizontal scale (the variable) is replaced with a logarithmic scale and plotting the cumulative probabilities of a skew distribution a straight line results. Such a graph paper is called logarithmic probability paper.

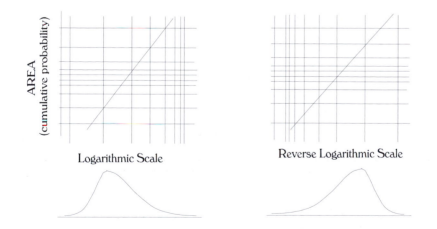

**Figure 106** Use logarithmic probability paper for skew distributions

Apart from the ability to demonstrate normality, the use of probability paper also provides a means to estimate the arithmetic mean and the standard deviation. Since the area within $\pm 1\sigma$ is known to correspond to 68% of the area, i.e 32% divided equally

289

above and below $\pm 1\sigma$ respectively. The standard deviation can therefore be estimated by taking the distance between 50% and 16%.

Although probability paper is commercially available, probability paper is often combined into a complete statistical record chart for ease of use.

Consider the following example.

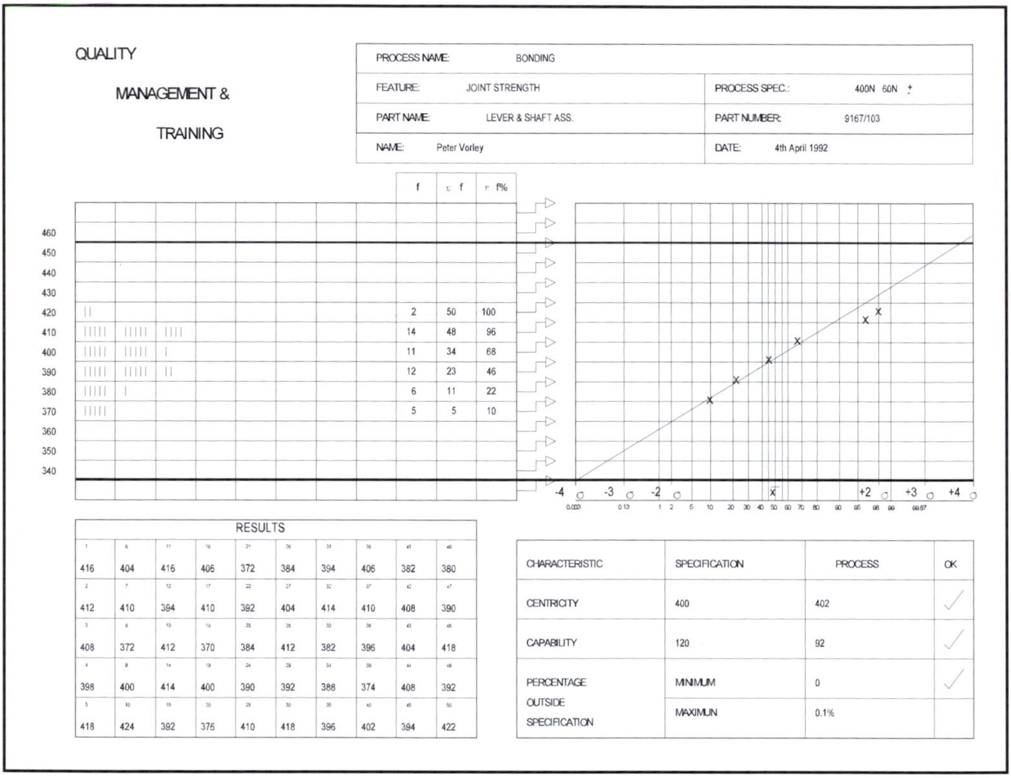


RESULTS

| | | | | | | | | | |
|---|---|---|---|---|---|---|---|---|---|
| 1<br>416 | 6<br>404 | 11<br>416 | 16<br>406 | 21<br>372 | 26<br>384 | 31<br>394 | 36<br>406 | 41<br>382 | 46<br>380 |
| 2<br>412 | 7<br>410 | 12<br>394 | 17<br>410 | 22<br>392 | 27<br>404 | 32<br>414 | 37<br>410 | 42<br>408 | 47<br>390 |
| 3<br>408 | 8<br>372 | 13<br>412 | 18<br>370 | 23<br>384 | 28<br>412 | 33<br>382 | 38<br>396 | 43<br>404 | 48<br>418 |
| 4<br>398 | 9<br>400 | 14<br>414 | 19<br>400 | 24<br>390 | 29<br>392 | 34<br>388 | 39<br>374 | 44<br>408 | 49<br>392 |
| 5<br>418 | 10<br>424 | 15<br>392 | 20<br>376 | 25<br>410 | 30<br>418 | 35<br>396 | 40<br>402 | 45<br>394 | 50<br>422 |

| CHARACTERISTIC | SPECIFICATION | PROCESS | OK |
|---|---|---|---|
| CENTRICITY | 400 | 402 | ✓ |
| CAPABILITY | 120 | 92 | ✓ |
| PERCENTAGE OUTSIDE SPECIFICATION | MINIMUM | 0 | ✓ |
| | MAXIMUN | 0.1% | |

**Figure 107** Completed Process Capability Chart

(1) Enter the process results in the sequence that they were produced.

(2) Determine the scale to be used. Experience has shown that the formula shown next for class interval can be used as a guide.

$$Classs\ Interval\ =\ \frac{Largest\ Reading\ -\ Smallest\ Reading}{8}$$

(64)

$$\frac{424\ -\ 370}{8}\ \approx\ 6.7$$

(65)

*for convenience use a class interval of 10N*

(3)   Draw in the tolerance or process specification limits in a thick black line across the complete width of the chart.  Enter the results on the tally chart.

(4)   Enter the frequency of each result in the column 'f' (zero if no value is found).

(5)   Working upwards in column 'Σf' calculate the cumulative frequency (Note Σ means the sum of or cumulation).

(6)   Convert the cumulative frequencies 'Σf' into percentages of the total and enter the result in column 'Σf%'.

(7)   Noting the bottom figure in column 'Σf%' follow the arrow until the corresponding point on the probability graph is found.  Mark this point with a cross. Repeat this exercise until the 100% figure is reached.  To avoid losing this last number the average of the last two figures can be plotted, eg.

$$\frac{Last\ Reading\ +\ Second\ to\ Last\ Reading}{2}$$

$$\frac{100+96}{2}\ =\ 98$$

(66)

*plot as 98% @ 425N*

# Variability

(8)  Draw the best fit straight line through all the points (extend the line to the extremities of the graph paper). If a reasonable fit cannot be found (your own judgement is required here), then the data may contain some non random effect or be zero limited. In these circumstances either identify the non random effect or use special skewed distribution paper.

(9)  To estimate the process mean for a normal distribution, i.e. if the line is straight, simply construct a vertical line from the 50% mark up to the plotted line and project a horizontal line across to the variable scale.

(10)  To estimate the standard deviation proceed as for the mean except project vertically from the 16%[21] position instead of the 50% position. Read off the corresponding value on the vertical scale, subtract this from the mean and the difference is the standard deviation.

---

[21]  See *Murdoch and Barnes Statistical Tables*, Area under the Tail of the Distribution. The area corresponding to 1.0 standard deviation is given as 0.1587 or approximately 16%

# Introduction to Quality

## The Binomial Distribution

Up to now, variables and their distribution have been considered. For attributes the measure is a number or proportion of defects or defectives. For this reason, another type of distribution - the Binomial Distribution, will now be considered. This distribution approximates to a normal distribution and can be used to calculate probabilities of defects or defectives.

The Binomial Theorem may be used whenever a series of trials satisfies the following conditions:

(a) There are only two possible outcomes in each trial which are mutually exclusive. These outcomes may be success and failure, defective and non-defective, go or not go, etc.

(b) The probability of success in each trial is constant. The probability of success is usually denoted by p and the probability of failure is usually denoted by:

$$p = 1 - q$$

(c) The outcomes of successive trials are mutually independent. This condition is met approximately when items are selected from a large batch and classified as defective and non-defective.

Consider a simple practical experiment, first of all to compare statistical theory with practice, and secondly to introduce the binomial theorem.

# Variability

*Practical exercise*

Take three coins and toss them in the air 1,000 times - note the number of occasions when there are no heads, 1 head, two heads and three heads in three using the following table:

Theoretical frequency

| Probability of a head | = | H | = | 1/2 |
|---|---|---|---|---|
| Probability of a tail | = | T | = | 1/2 |

Listing all the possibilities:

OH   T x T x T = ½ x ½ x ½ = ⅛ = 0.125

1H   H x T x T = ½ x ½ x ½ = ⅛ }
     T x H x T = ½ x ½ x ½ = ⅛ } = ⅜ = 0.375
     T x T x H = ½ x ½ x ½ = ⅛ }

2H   T x H x H = ½ x ½ x ½ = ⅛ }
     H x H x T = ½ x ½ x ½ = ⅛ } = ⅜ = 0.375
     H x T x H = ½ x ½ x ½ = ⅛ }

3H   H x H x H = ½ x ½ x ½ = ⅛ } = <u>0.125</u>

                                  Total = 1.000

Tally chart:

| Number of heads | Frequency | Total Empirical frequency | Theoretical frequency |
|---|---|---|---|
| 0H (no heads) | | | 125 |
| 1H (1 head) | | | 375 |
| 2H (2 heads) | | | 375 |
| 3H (3 heads) | | | 125 |
| | | 1000 | 1000 |

Formalising this a general expression for theoretical probabilities may be determined.

The formulations are:

| | | | | |
|---|---|---|---|---|
| OH | TTT | = | $T^3$ | $T^3$ |
| 1H | HTT | = | $T^2H$ } | |
| | THT | = | $T^2H$ } | $3T^2H$ |
| | TTH | = | $T^2H$ } | |
| 2H | THH | = | $TH^2$ } | |
| | HHT | = | $TH^2$ } | $3TH^2$ |
| | HTH | = | $TH^2$ } | |
| 3H | HHH | = | H | $H^3$ |

Since the combined probabilities is 1.0

$$T^3 + 3T^2H + 3TH^2 + H^3 = 1$$

$T^3 + 3T^2H + 3TH^2 + H^3$   is an expansion of $(T + H)^3$ called a binomial expansion.

295

# Variability

The respective probabilities of OH, 1H, 2H and 3H will be the corresponding terms of the expansion $T^3 + 3T^2H + 3TH^2 + H^3$

In general, we can say that the probabilities of x heads will be

$$P_x = c_x T^{n-x} H^x$$

Where $c_x$ is a co-efficient for the respective number of events (heads).

$$c_x = \frac{n!}{x!\,(n-x)!}$$

Where n! stands for n factorial, all numbers from 1 to n multiplied together.

e.g. $5! = 1 \times 2 \times 3 \times 4 \times 5 = 120$

$$\therefore P_x = \frac{n!}{x!\,(n-x)!} T^{n-x} H^x$$

Example: Calculate the probability of 0, 1, 2, 3, 4, 5, heads when tossing 5 coins.

$$
\begin{aligned}
(T+H)^5 &= \frac{5!}{0!\,(5-0)!} T^{5-0}H^0 + \frac{5!}{1!\,(5-1)!} T^{5-1}H^1 + \frac{5!}{2!\,(5-2)!} T^{5-2}H^2 \\
&\quad + \frac{5!}{3!\,(5-3)!} T^{5-3}H^3 + \frac{5!}{4!\,(5-4)!} T^{5-4}H^4 + \frac{5!}{x!\,(5-5)!} T^{5-5}H^5 \\
&= \frac{5!}{0!5!} T^5 H^0 + \frac{5!}{1!4!} T^4 H^1 + \frac{5!}{2!\,3!} T^3 H^2 + \frac{5!}{3!\,2!} T^2 H^3 + \frac{5!}{4!\,1!} T^1 H^4 + \frac{5!}{5!\,0!} T^0 H^5 \\
&= T^5 + \frac{120}{24} T^4 H^1 + \frac{120}{2\times 6} T^3 H^2 + \frac{120}{6\times 2} T^2 H^3 + \frac{120}{24} T^1 H^4 + H^5 \\
&= T^5 + 5T^4 H^1 + 10T^3 H^2 + 10T^2 H^3 + 5T^1 H^4 + H^5 \\
&= 0.5^5 + 5\times 0.5^4 \times 0.5^1 + 10\times 0.5^3 0.5^2 + 10\times 0.5^2 0.5^3 + 5\times 0.5^1 0.5^4 + 0.5^5 \\
&= 0.03125 + 0.15625 + 0.3125 + 0.3125 + 0.15625 + 0.03125
\end{aligned}
$$

Thus for 1000 trials, tosses of the coins $(T + H)^5$ comes out as:

| OH | 1H. | 2H | 3H | 4H | 5H |
|---|---|---|---|---|---|
| 32.15 | 156.25 | 312.5 | 312.5 | 156.25 | 31.25 |

Ex. Calculate the probability of 0 or 1 heads

| | |
|---|---|
| 0.03125 | OH |
| 0.15625 | 1H |
| 0.18750 | |

Ex. Calculate the probability of 0, 1 or 2 heads

| | |
|---|---|
| 0.03125 | OH |
| 0.15625 | 1H |
| 0.31250 | 2H |
| 0.50000 | |

# Variability

Instead of using formulae to ascertain the binomial co-efficients, providing the expansion is symmetrical, the binomial co-efficients can be found using Pascal's triangle as follows:

Value of n                    Numerical co-efficients in the expansion of $(p + q)^n$

### Pascal's Triangle

| | | | | | | | | | | | | | | | |
|---|---|---|---|---|---|---|---|---|---|---|---|---|---|---|---|
| | | | | | | | 1 | | | | | | | | |
| 1 | | | | | | 1 | | 1 | | | | | | | |
| 2 | | | | | 1 | | 2 | | 1 | | | | | | |
| 3 | | | | 1 | | 3 | | 3 | | 1 | | | | | |
| 4 | | | 1 | | 4 | | 6 | | 4 | | 1 | | | | |
| 5 | | 1 | | 5 | | 10 | | 10 | | 5 | | 1 | | | |
| 6 | 1 | | 6 | | 15 | | 20 | | 15 | | 6 | | 1 | | |
| 7 | | 1 | | 7 | 21 | | 35 | | 35 | | 21 | | 7 | | 1 |
| 8 | 1 | | 8 | 28 | | 56 | 70 | | 56 | | 28 | | 8 | | 1 |

Numerical coefficients in the expansion of $(q + p)^n$

Notice that the construction of this chart is based on each number being the sum of the two numbers above it, i.e. referring to the bottom row $1 = 0 + 1$, $8 = 1 + 7$, $28 = 7 + 21$ etc.

In quality control the symbols Q and P are used; Q for a good component P for a defective component. When $Q = P = 0.5$ the results are similar to $(T + H)^n$ where $T = H = 0.5$.

When the probabilities of success and failure are equal (0.5) then a symmetrical distribution which approximates to the normal distribution is produced.

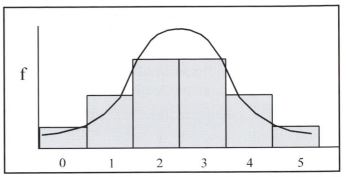

f

0    1    2    3    4    5

**Figure 108** Probability distribution of heads & tails for 5 coins

In practice, it is realistic to assume that the defectives in a sample or batch will be quite small, e.g. Q = 0.9 P = 0.1

## Example 1

It is known that 10% of the resistors produced by a certain process are defective. From a large batch a sample of five resistors is taken at random. Find the probabilities of obtaining 0, 1, 2, 3, 4 and 5 defective resistors in the sample and draw a histogram to represent these probabilities.

The probability of a single resistor, chosen at random, being defective is

$$p = \frac{10}{100} = 0.1$$

The probability of it being good is     $q = 1 - p = 0.9$

The number in the sample is     $n = 5$

Now     $(q + p)^5 = q^5 + 5q^4p + 10q^3p^2 + 10q^2p^3 + 5qp^4 + p^5$

# Variability

The probabilities are shown in the table below and the histogram that follows.

| Number of defectives in the sample | Term of expansion | Probability | |
|---|---|---|---|
| 0 | $q^5$ | $(0.9)^5$ | $= 0.59049$ |
| 1 | $5q^4p$ | $5 \times (0.9)^4 \times (0.1)$ | $= 0.32805$ |
| 2 | $10q^3p^2$ | $10 \times (0.9)^3 \times (0.1)^2$ | $= 0.07290$ |
| 3 | $10q^2p^3$ | $10 \times (0.9)^2 \times (0.1)^3$ | $= 0.00810$ |
| 4 | $5qp^4$ | $5 \times (0.9) \times (0.1)^4$ | $= 0.00045$ |
| 5 | $p^5$ | $(0.1)^5$ | $= 0.00001$ |

Total probability covering all possible events =     1.00000

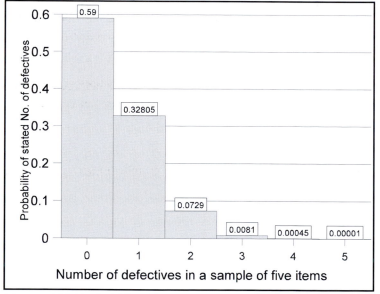

**Figure 109** Probability distribution

# Introduction to Quality

## Example 2

Cartons which contain four items each are checked and it is found that 8% of the items are defective. If 10,000 cartons are purchased find:

a)  How many cartons are expected to have no defective items.

b)  How many cartons are expected to have one defective item.

c)  How many cartons are expected to have less than two defective items.

d)  How many defective items there are likely to be in the 10,000 cartons.

## Solutions

a)  If one carton is selected at random then the probability of it containing no defective items is given by the first term of $(q + p)^4$ which is $q^4$. Since $p = 0.08$, then $q = 0.92$ and $q^4 = (0.92)^4 = 0.7164$ the number of cartons containing no defective items is expected to be $0.7164 \times 10,000 = 7,164$.

b)  The probability of finding a carton with one defective item in it is the second term of $(q + p)^4$, i.e. $4q^3p = 4 \times (0.92)^3 \times 0.08 = 0.2492$. The number of cartons with 1 defective item is expected to be $0.2492 \times 10,000 = 2,492$.

c)  The number of cartons containing less than two defective items (i.e. containing no defective items or containing one defective item) is expected to be $7,164 + 2,492 = 9,656$.

d)  The number of defective items in the 10,000 boxes is expected to be $4 \times 10,000 \times 0.08 = 3,200$.

# Variability

## Example 3

A machine is known to produce 10% of defective parts.  Samples of four items are taken from the batches produced and examined.  If 1,000 samples are checked, draw a histogram showing the number of defectives which are to be expected.

Here    $p = 0.1$,  $q = 1 - p = 0.9$  and  $n = 4$.

$$(q + p)^4 = q^4 + 4q^3p + 6q^2p^2 + 4qp^3 + p^4$$

The distribution is shown in the following table:

| Number of defectives in the sample | Term of the binomial expansion | Probability of the stated number of defectives being found in the sample | | Number of samples with the stated number of defectives | |
|---|---|---|---|---|---|
| 0 | $q^4$ | $(0.9)^4$ | $= 0.656$ | $1{,}000 \times 0.656$ | $= 656$ |
| 1 | $4q^3p$ | $4 \times (0.9)^3 \times (0.1)$ | $= 0.292$ | $1{,}000 \times 0.292$ | $= 292$ |
| 2 | $6q^2p^2$ | $6 \times (0.9)^2 \times (0.1)^2$ | $= 0.049$ | $1{,}000 \times 0.049$ | $= 49$ |
| 3 | $4qp^3$ | $4 \times (0.9) \times (0.1)^3$ | $= 0.003$ | $1{,}000 \times 0.003$ | $= 3$ |
| 4 | $p^4$ | $(0.1)^4$ | $= 0.0001$ | $1{,}000 \times 0.0001$ | $= 0.1$ |

The histogram below represents the distribution.

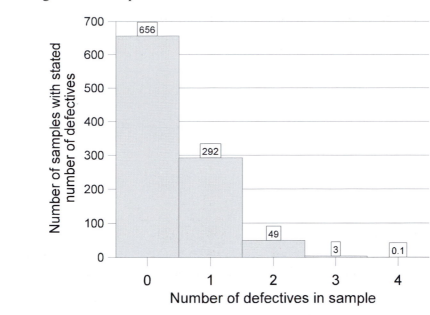

**Figure 110** Probability distribution

# Variability

## Example 4

Eight coins are tossed together 256 times. Draw up a theoretical frequency table for the number of heads which may be expected and hence construct a histogram to represent the theoretical frequency distribution.

Here $p = \frac{1}{2}$, $q = \frac{1}{2}$ and $n = 8$

$$(q + p)^8 = q^8 + 8q^7p + 28q^6p^2 + 56q^5p^3 + 70q^4p^4 + 56q^3p^5 + 28q^2p^6 + 8qp^7 + p^8$$

The histogram of the theoretical frequencies distribution is shown in **Figure 111**.

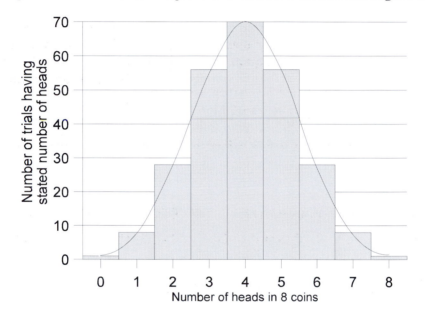

**Figure 111** Histogram of the distribution of theoretical frequencies

Comparing **Figure 110** with **Figure 111**, the distribution in **Figure 110** is skewed to the right whilst that of **Figure 111** is symmetrical. A histogram of a binomial distribution is symmetrical if, and only if, $p = q = 1/2$.

However when $np$ is greater than 5 the histogram is reasonably symmetrical, but for values of $np$ less than 5 the histogram will be noticeably skewed.

## Example 5

It is known that a certain process produces 10% of defective articles. If a sample of 20 items is taken at random from a large batch of articles, find the probability of the sample containing two or more defective items.

Here $p = 0.1$ and $q = 0.9$. Since $n = 20$ we require the first two terms of the expansion of $(q + p)^{20}$.

| Number of defective items in the sample | Term of the expansion | Probability of obtaining the stated number of defective items in the sample | |
|:---:|:---:|:---|:---|
| 0 | $q^{20}$ | $(0.9)^{20}$ | $= 0.1216$ |
| 1 | $20q^{19}p$ | $20 \times (0.9)^{19} \times (0.1)$ | $= 0.2702$ |

| | | | | | |
|---|---|---|---|---|---|
| Pr(less than 2) | $=$ | Pr(0) + Pr(1) | $=$ 0.1216 + 0.2702 | $=$ | 0.3918 |
| Pr(2 or more) | $=$ | 1 - Pr(less than 2) | $=$ 1 - 0.3918 | $=$ | 0.6082 |

Since the total probability covering all possible events is 1.

# Variability

## The mean and standard deviation of a binomial distribution

Since the binomial distribution approximates to a normal distribution it may be used to construct a control chart for attributes based on the same principles as for variables. However, we need to know the statistics of the distribution.

It can be proved that the mean and standard deviation for a binomial distribution are given by:

$$\bar{X} = np \qquad \text{and} \qquad \sigma = \sqrt{npq}$$

## Example 6

A production process is 6% defective. From a large batch a sample of 200 items is taken. Calculate the mean number of defectives in the sample and the standard deviation.

$$\bar{x} = np = 200 \times 0.06 = 12$$

$$\sigma = \sqrt{npq} = \sqrt{200 \times 0.06 \times 0.94} = 3.36$$

**The Poisson Distribution**

A limitation of the binomial distribution is that it is necessary know the value of n the sample size. There are, however, many cases where the value of *n* is not known, for instance, in checking the number of weaving defects in a length of cloth or the number of welding defects in a welded assembly. Another distribution which provides us with a means of calculating probabilities is the Poisson distribution. It is based on the series for the natural number $e^{22}$. The Poisson distribution may be used to determine probabilities provided that $\lambda$ is made equal to the average value of the occurrence of the event.

$$e^{\lambda} = 1 + \lambda + \frac{\lambda^2}{2!} + \frac{\lambda^3}{3!} + \ .....$$

In any calculations involving probabilities, the total probability covering all possible events must be equal to 1. Now

$$e^{\lambda} \ x \ e^{-\lambda} = e^0 = 1$$

Hence, the product $e^{\lambda}$ x $e^{-\lambda}$ can be used to form a theoretical frequency distribution when it is written in the form:

$$e^{-\lambda}(1 + \lambda + \frac{\lambda^2}{2!} + \frac{\lambda^3}{3!} + \ ......)$$

Where each term represents the probability of 0, 1, 2, 3, 4 etc. defectives given that the expected average number of defectives (np) is $\lambda$.

---

[22]  e is called a natural number since its occurrence, like $\pi$ is found in the laws of many natural phenomena including electromagnetism. Its value is approximately 2.7183. It is also referred to as the exponential number.

# Variability

A distribution obtained by using this series is called a Poisson distribution. Tables of values of $e^{-x}$ are available in most books of mathematical tables. Values are also easily found by entering a number in a scientific calculator and pressing the exponential key (often labelled $e^x$).

## Example 1

A process is known to produce 2% of defective items. A sample of 100 items is drawn at random from a large batch of these items. Find the probabilities of obtaining 0, 1, 2, and 3 defective items in the sample.

Here    $p = 0.02$  and  $n = 100$

Hence  $\lambda = np = 100 \times 0.02 = 2$

Using a calculator or referring to tables of $e^{-x}$,  $e^{-2} = 0.1353$

## Relation between the Poisson and binomial distributions

In the binomial distribution if $n$ (the number of items in a sample) is large and $p$ (the fraction defective) is small then the event of finding a defective item in the sample is called a *rare event*.

In practice if $n \geq 50$ and $np < 5$ the event may be considered rare. In such cases the Poisson distribution gives a very close approximation to the binomial distribution.

Generally the approximation between a binomial and Poisson distribution is good if $p \leq 0.1$ and $np \leq 5$.

**Using the Poisson distribution as an approximation to the binomial distribution**

In the majority of cases, the fraction defective, $p$, is usually small. If a sample of $n$ items is taken from a batch of such items, the expected number of defectives in the sample will be $\lambda = np$. Hence the Poisson distribution may be used as an approximation to the binomial distribution, if $\lambda$ represents the expected number of defectives in a sample of $n$ items.

The probability of obtaining 0 defectives $\quad Pr(0) = e^{-\lambda} \times 1 = e^{-\lambda}$

The probability of obtaining 1 defective $\quad Pr(1) = e^{-\lambda} \times \lambda = \lambda e^{-\lambda}$

The probability of obtaining 2 defectives $\quad Pr(2) = e^{-\lambda} \times \dfrac{\lambda^2}{2!} = \dfrac{\lambda^2}{2!} e$

The probability of obtaining 3 defectives $\quad Pr(3) = e^{-\lambda} \times \dfrac{\lambda^3}{3!} = \dfrac{\lambda^3}{3!} e$

etc.

| Number of defective items in the sample | Probability of obtaining the stated number of defective items in the sample |
|:---:|:---:|
| 0 | $Pr(0) = e^{-\lambda} = 0.1353$ |
| 1 | $Pr(1) = \lambda e^{-\lambda} = \lambda\, Pr(0) = 2 \times 0.1353 = 0.2706$ |
| 2 | $Pr(2) = \dfrac{\lambda^2}{2!} e^{-\lambda} = \dfrac{\lambda}{2} Pr(1) = \dfrac{2}{2} \times 0.2706 = 0.2706$ |
| 3 | $Pr(3) = \dfrac{\lambda^3}{3!} e^{-\lambda} = \dfrac{\lambda}{3} Pr(2) = \dfrac{2}{3} \times 0.2706 = 0.1804$ |

**Example 2**

It is known that a certain process produces 8% of defective items. A sample of 50 items is drawn from a large batch produced by the process. Find the probabilities of finding 0,1 and 2 defective items in the sample by using:

a)     the Poisson distribution.

b)     the binomial distribution.

a)     For the Poisson distribution $p = 0.08$ and $n = 50$

$$\therefore \quad \lambda \; = \; np \; = \; 50 \times 0.08 \; = \; 4$$
$$e^{-\lambda} \; = \; e^{-4} \; = \; 0.0183$$

b)     For the binomial distribution $p = 0.08$, $q = 0.92$ and $n = 50$

$$(q + p)^{50} \; = \; q^{50} \; + \; 50q^{49}p \; + \; \frac{50 \times 49}{2!} q^{48}p^2 \; ....$$
$$= \; q^{50} \; + \; 50q^{49}p \; + \; 1225q^{48}p^2 \; ....$$

| Number Of Defectives In Sample | Probability | |
| :---: | :---: | :---: |
| | Poisson | Binomial |
| 0 | $e^{-\lambda} = 0.0183$ | $q^{50} = (0.92)^{50} = 0.0155$ |
| 1 | $\lambda\, e^{-\lambda} = 0.0732$ | $50 q^{49} p = 0.0672$ |
| 2 | $\dfrac{\lambda^2}{2!}\, e^{-\lambda} = 0.1464$ | $1225 q^{48} p^2 = 0.1433$ |

On comparing the probabilities as calculated for both the Poisson and binomial distributions, it will be seen that the Poisson distribution is a reasonable approximation to the binomial distribution.

## Example 3

A process produces 3% of defective articles.  From a large batch of these articles a sample of 80 items is taken.  Find the probability that the sample will contain two or more defective items.

Here $p = 0.03$ and $n = 80$

Hence $\quad\quad \lambda = np = 80 \times 0.03 = 2.4$

$\quad\quad\quad\quad\quad e^{-\lambda} = e^{-2.4} = 0.0907$

| Number of defective articles in the sample | Probability |
|---|---|
| 0 | $Pr(0) = e^{-\lambda} = 0.0907$ |
| 1 | $Pr(1) = \lambda Pr(0) = 0.2177$ |

The Probability of 1 or less defective items in the sample
$$= 0.0907 + 0.2177 = 0.3084$$

Hence the probability of two or more defective items in the sample
$$= 1 - 0.3084 = 0.6916$$

## Example 4

On checking several cartons containing large numbers of bolts, it was found that the average number of defective bolts in a carton was two.  Find the probability of finding a box containing three or more defective bolts.

Here $\lambda = 2$ and $e^{-\lambda} = 0.1353$

| Number of defective bolts in the carton | Probability |
|---|---|
| 0 | $Pr(0) = \quad e^{-\lambda} = 0.1353$ |
| 1 | $Pr(1) = \quad \lambda Pr(0) \quad = 0.2707$ |
| 2 | $Pr(2) = \quad \dfrac{\lambda}{2}Pr(1) = 0.2707$ |

Probability of two or less defective bolts in a carton

$= 0.1353 + 0.2707 + 0.2707 = 0.6767$

Hence the probability of three or more defective bolts in a carton

$= 1 - 0.6767 = 0.3233$

It is likely, therefore, that 32.33% of all the cartons will contain three or more defective bolts.

## Example 5

20 sheets of aluminium alloy were examined for surface flaws. The number of flaws per sheet were as follows:

| Sheet number | 0 | 1 | 2 | 3 | 4 | 5 | 6 | 7 | 8 | 9 | 10 |
|---|---|---|---|---|---|---|---|---|---|---|---|
| Number of flaws | 4 | 0 | 2 | 6 | 4 | 2 | 0 | 0 | 2 | 0 | 4 |

| Sheet number | 11 | 12 | 13 | 14 | 15 | 16 | 17 | 18 | 19 | 20 |
|---|---|---|---|---|---|---|---|---|---|---|
| Number of flaws | 4 | 2 | 1 | 3 | 4 | 1 | 1 | 5 | 3 | 2 |

# Variability

Find the probability of finding a sheet, chosen at random from a batch of these sheets, which contains three or more surface flaws.

$$\lambda = \text{ the average number of flaws per sheet } = \frac{total\ number\ of\ flaws}{number\ of\ sheets\ checked}$$

$$= \frac{50}{20} = 2.5$$

| Number of flaws per sheet | Probability | | |
|---|---|---|---|
| 0 | $Pr(0) =$ | $e^{-\lambda}$ | $= 0.0821$ |
| 1 | $Pr(1) =$ | $\lambda Pr(0)$ | $= 0.2052$ |
| 2 | $Pr(2) =$ | $\frac{\lambda}{2} Pr(1)$ | $= 0.2565$ |

Probability of finding a sheet with three or more surface flaws

$$= 1 - (0.0821 + 0.2052 + 0.2565) = 0.4562$$

Hence it is likely that 45.62% of the sheets in the batch will contain 3 or more surface flaws.

# Introduction to Quality

**The mean and standard deviation of a Poisson distribution**

As with the binomial distribution it can be shown that the mean and standard deviation of a Poisson distribution are:

$$\bar{X} = \lambda \quad \text{and} \quad \sigma = \sqrt{\lambda}$$

**Example 6**

The following table shows the frequency of accidents in a factory during a 100 day period. Calculate the mean and standard deviation for this distribution. Show that the distribution is well represented by a Poisson distribution.

| Number of accidents | 0 | 1 | 2 | 3 | 4 |
|---|---|---|---|---|---|
| Number of days on which this number of accidents occurred | 42 | 36 | 14 | 6 | 2 |

| Number of accidents = $x$ | Frequency = $f$ | $fx$ | $fx^2$ |
|---|---|---|---|
| 0 | 42 | 0 | 0 |
| 1 | 36 | 36 | 36 |
| 2 | 14 | 28 | 56 |
| 3 | 6 | 18 | 54 |
| 4 | 2 | 8 | 32 |
| | 100 | 90 | 178 |

$$\bar{x} = \frac{90}{100} = 0.9 \qquad \sigma = \sqrt{\frac{178}{100} - (0.9)^2} = 0.985$$

315

# Variability

Taking $\lambda = 0.9$, $\quad e^{-\lambda} = 0.4066$

| Number of accidents | Probability | Expected number of days<br>= probability x 100 |
|---|---|---|
| 0 | $Pr(0) = e^{-\lambda} = 0.4066$ | $40.66 \approx 41$ |
| 1 | $Pr(1) = \lambda Pr(0) = 0.3659$ | $36.59 \approx 37$ |
| 2 | $Pr(2) = \frac{\lambda}{2}Pr(1) = 0.1647$ | $16.47 \approx 16$ |
| 3 | $Pr(3) = \frac{\lambda}{2}Pr(2) = 0.0494$ | $4.94 \approx 5$ |
| 4 | $Pr(4) = \frac{\lambda}{4}Pr(3) = 0.0$ | $1.11 \approx 1$ |

Hence the given distribution is well represented by a Poisson distribution with $\lambda = 0.9$. The standard deviation of the Poisson distribution is:

$$\sigma = \sqrt{\lambda} = \sqrt{0.9} = 0.949$$

this agrees very well with the value calculated previously.

## Statistical Tolerancing

Precision is cost related. Tighter tolerances usually mean higher costs. Statistical Tolerancing is a method of avoiding specifying unnecessarily tight tolerances. When assemblies consist of several mating components the designer will usually select tolerances for the individual components that will make tolerance clashes impossible. This is an understandable decision as it avoids any problems in assembling the finished product. However, in practice the designer is worrying unnecessarily because the chance of such a tolerance clash condition actually occurring is very remote. This is because statistically, the sum of the tolerances is unlikely to be equal to the arithmetical sum. This is due to the fact that, given that the component sizes are normally distributed, the chances of every component in the assembly being at one extreme limit is very remote.

Consider the following example.

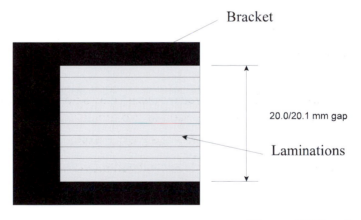

Bracket

20.0/20.1 mm gap

Laminations

**Figure 112** Lamination

**Figure 112** shows a bracket which contains 10 laminations. The 10 laminations fit inside a bracket with a 20/20.1mm gap. If the designer uses arithmetical tolerances then the following equation would apply.

$$\frac{Total\ tolerance}{Number\ of\ Components} = Component\ Tolerance = \frac{0.1}{10} = 0.01mm \qquad (97)$$

317

# Variability

In effect this means that each lamination must be between 2.00 to 2.01mm in size. Such a tolerance would only be necessary if all laminations were at one extreme which is a very unlikely event.

Statistical tolerancing takes into consideration that this is a very unlikely event. If statistical tolerancing was applied to this example then the tolerance could be much greater.

From the section on Process Capability Studies, it was suggested that for process capability the process specification should be equal to or greater than six standard deviations.

It can be shown that the total variance equals the sum of the individual variance.

$$\sigma_t^2 = \sigma_1^2 + \sigma_2^2 + \sigma_3^2 + \sigma_4^2 + \ldots\ldots\ldots \sigma_n^2$$

*Where $\sigma_1^2$, $\sigma_2^2$, $\sigma_3^2$, $\sigma_4^2$, $\ldots\ldots\ldots$ $\sigma_n^2$*

**(98)**

*are the individual standard deviations of each component*

*and $\sigma_t$ is the total standard deviation*

Now if the tolerance $= 6\sigma$ then we can substitute T for $\sigma$ thus:

$$T_t^2 = T_1^2 + T_2^2 + T_3^2 + T_4^2 + \ldots\ldots\ldots\ldots T_n^2 \qquad \textbf{(99)}$$

Where the individual tolerances are equal then this reduces to:

$$T_t^2 = T_i^2 * n$$

$$or \quad T_i = T_t * \sqrt{\frac{1}{n}}$$

*Where* **(100)**

$$T_i = The\ individual\ tolerance$$
$$T_t = The\ total\ tolerance$$
$$n = The\ number\ of\ items$$

For the lamination example, the tolerance for each individual lamination would be:

$$T_i = 0.1 * \sqrt{\frac{1}{10}} = 0.032mm \qquad \textbf{(101)}$$

This tolerance (0.032mm) is obviously an improvement on the 0.01mm which was given by arithmetical tolerancing. Statistical tolerancing can provide cost and time savings. In the example the tolerance is now over three times larger, with probably no effect on the overall assembly performance.

*Assumptions for statistical tolerancing to be viable*

The process needs to be capable, the process distribution needs to be normal, and vary equally around the mean. The components must be randomly selected. If these criteria are not met then these principles may not apply.

Following are some other examples of the application of statistical tolerancing.

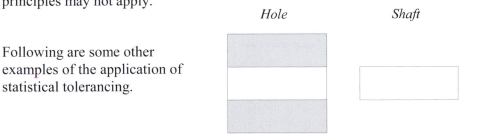

*Hole*          *Shaft*

*Clearance between hole & Shaft = 0.01/0.05mm*

**Figure 113**

## Variability

The first example is of a hole and shaft. The clearance between the hole and the shaft needs to be 0.01 to 0.05mm. Sharing the arithmetical tolerance equally between the hole and shaft would mean that the hole and shaft tolerance would be 0.02mm each.

However, if the statistical tolerancing equation is used then the tolerance becomes 0.028mm.

$$\textit{Individual tolerance } T_i \ = \ 0.04 \ * \ \sqrt{\frac{1}{2}} \ = \ 0.028mm \qquad \textbf{(102)}$$

The second example is where a complete bar length is made up of three individual bars of various length and tolerance.

$$9.9/10.1 \qquad 14.8/15.2 \qquad 4.6/5.4$$

### Bar length

**Figure 114** Three bars

The arithmetical variation in bar length will be 0.2+0.4+0.8 = 1.4mm

The statistical variation in bar length will be:

$$T_t^2 = \ 0.2^2 \ + \ 0.4^2 \ + \ 0.8^2$$
$$T_t = \ 0.92mm \qquad \qquad \textbf{(103)}$$

As previously explained, there are benefits to be gained from the use of statistical tolerancing but there are also dangers. It is important that the process is confirmed to be capable, otherwise the calculation may be in error.

## Operating Characteristic Curves

*Statistical Sampling using published Acceptance Plans*

There are two fundamental risks when inspecting:

    i.            Accepting a defective batch.

    ii.           Rejecting a good batch.

These are referred to as the Consumers' Risk and Producers' Risk respectively.

These risks may occur with 100% inspection as well as with sampling inspection. With 100% inspection the risk is referred to as uncertainty and includes inspection errors such as inspector fatigue. This latter risk is still present with sampling but is very much reduced owing to the lower volume of repetitive inspection.

However, when sampling, there is another risk that an individual sample might not truly represent the batch. The sample may have a smaller percentage of defectives than the batch or vice-versa. In other words, the sample may give us an optimistic picture of the batch causing a risk for the consumer, or a pessimistic picture of the batch causing a corresponding risk for the producer. Sampling plans based on statistical theory allow us to calculate these risks.

During the Second World War, two statisticians in America, Dodge and Romig, spent many months calculating these risks. They examined the effect of varying the sample size (n) and varying the acceptance criteria (c) (the acceptable number of defectives in the sample). Each combination was called a sample plan. For example, 'take a sample of 125 items and if there are no more than three defectives in the sample then accept the whole batch otherwise reject the whole batch'.

Using probability theory, the probability of accepting a batch of items containing x% defectives can be calculated. Performing this calculation for x = 0 to say 10%, a probability curve is derived known as the Operating Characteristic Curve (OCC). Every combination of sample size and acceptance number will have its own unique Operating Characteristic Curve.

# Variability

The one shown here is for a sample size of 125 and accept the batch if 3 or less defectives and reject the batch if 4 or more.

*Producer's Risk and the Acceptable Quality Level*

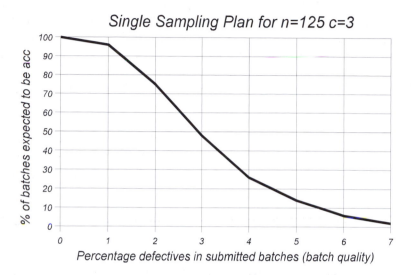

**Figure 115** Operating Characteristic Curve

Notice that this curve suggests that there is a 95% probability that a batch containing 1% defectives would be accepted, or put another way 95% of batches containing 1% defectives would be accepted, i.e. there is a Producer's Risk of 5%. This would give a high degree of confidence over a period of time that the average level of defects would be 1% or lower. This is referred to as the AQL - Acceptable Quality Level. Another way of stating this is that the AQL is "that batch quality for which the probability of acceptance is 0.95 (95%)", i.e. AQL = 1% on this particular operating curve.

The batch quality corresponding to the producer's risk is referred to as the Acceptable Quality Level (AQL). The producer's risk is often set at 5%.

*Consumer's Risk and Limiting Quality (LQ) or Lot Tolerance Percent Defective (LTPD)*

The OCC illustrates how a particular sampling plan would operate over a long period. While the batches arriving are of a quality equal to or better than the AQL the majority of batches will be accepted. However, there is still a probability that batches of worse quality than the AQL will also be accepted, i.e. the Consumer's Risk. As with all processes there is an allowable tolerance during operation. For statistical sampling it is the worst quality considered to be acceptable of a single batch. It is called the Limiting Quality (LQ) or the Lot[23] Tolerance Percent Defective (LTPD).

With reference to the sampling plan, there is a 10% risk that lots containing exactly 5.5% defectives will be accepted. The batch quality (5.5%) corresponding to the consumer's risk is therefore the Limiting Quality (LQ). The consumer's risk is often set at 10%.

Thus the above sampling plan - n =125, c = 3 corresponds to a sampling plan for an AQL of 1%. **Figure 116** shows the complete picture.

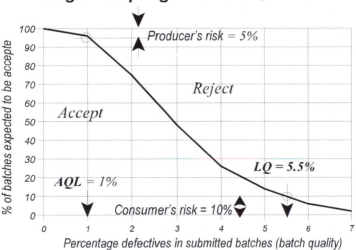

**Figure 116** Operating Characteristic Curve

---

[23]   Lot is the American term for batch. The term LQ is generally used in the UK while the term LTPD is generally used in the USA.

323

# Variability

## *Acceptance Sampling Plans*

The way these sampling plans work is that items are presented in batches. A representative sample is selected and inspected, and if the sample contains fewer than the reject number then the batch is accepted. If the sample contains a number of defectives equal to or more than the reject number, then the whole batch is rejected. Rejected batches would normally be subjected to 100% inspection to remove the defectives and re-submitted for sampling. This is called an Acceptance Sampling Plan.

An interesting observation from these studies shows that theoretically the batch size does not affect the risks. The risk pattern, the OCC, remains fixed regardless of batch size. In practice, there are other considerations to be taken into account:

i.      The fixed sample size means less inspection if items are treated as large batches but a rejected batch means it must be subjected to 100% inspection and consequentially delayed availability of the items for use.

ii.     The larger the batch, the more difficult it is to ensure a representative sample.

## *BS 6001*

The British Standards Institute has rationalised the selection of sampling plans from the infinite permutations and provided practical working tables to cover almost any eventuality. These sampling plans are published in BS 6001. BS 6000 provides a definitive guide to the theory, selection and application of sampling plans.

The selection of sampling plans in BS 6001 makes use of the preferred number principles covered in a previous unit. They also take into account the cost of inspection and, therefore, identify realistic sample sizes for varying batch sizes. It should be remembered, however, that risks are identical for a given sample size regardless of the batch size and these variations are intended to optimise the total amount of inspection, i.e. the combination of inspecting samples and 100% inspection of rejected batches.

*Switching rules*

Ideally, an OCC should be as near vertical as possible with 100% probability of accepting all batches better than the AQL and 0% probability of accepting batches worse than the AQL. This can be achieved to a degree by the use of so called 'switching rules'. Basically, this means that when batches are believed to be better than the AQL, the

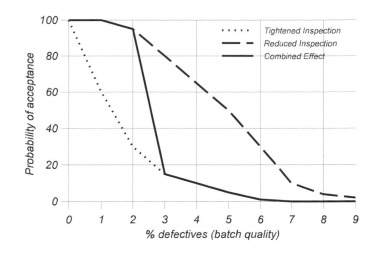

**Figure 117** Effect of switching rules on OCC

amount of inspection can be reduced. Conversely, when the quality of batches is believed to be worse than the AQL, the amount of inspection is increased or tightened. This approach can have the effect of combining two OCC's to give a much steeper curve approaching the ideal.

*Double, Multiple and Sequential Sampling Plans*

Another approach towards economising on sampling is to take smaller samples in the first instance. If the batch is either very good or very bad a decision can be made immediately without further sampling. However, if the percentage of defectives is close to the acceptable quality level then further samples may be taken to provide more information. Thus the single sampling plan can be modified to a double sampling plan. This is particularly economic when the quality is consistently good (or bad).

This principle can be extended to multiple sampling plans where up to seven stages of sampling may be needed to make a final decision. Much smaller sample sizes provide the prospect of an early decision when the quality of incoming goods is either very

# Variability

good or very bad. Continued sampling will be required only when the quality is borderline.

Indeed this principle can be taken to the extreme where the sample size is one. Samples are inspected until enough information has been gained to make a decision.

A word of caution is necessary when considering acceptance sampling. Sampling is based on what happens in the long run. While predictions about the long term performance of sampling plans is possible, variations between individual batches will be less certain in the short term and for single or short runs of supplies. In addition, sampling is based on random selection from homogeneous populations. Special techniques may be necessary to ensure this principle is maintained, such as 'stratification'. An example would be to take random samples from each package of a consignment rather than from the top package only.

## Cusum Charts

With a standard quality control chart, action is dependent upon individually plotted points. Although some trends may be detectable, generally no action will be taken so long as points lie within the control limits. Hence a run of points above or below the average may go unnoticed because the position of each point is independent of those which preceded it. This may be unsatisfactory as it could be that the average value over a period is the important factor, rather than individual values.

The technique which uses all available information and is more sensitive to short and long term changes and trends, even small but persistent changes, is the *Cumulative Sum Chart*, or *CUSUM* as it is called. This type of chart was developed in Britain in the 1950's and is one of the most powerful management tools available for the detection of trends and slight changes in data.

The Cusum chart is, therefore, a much more sensitive device in detecting changes in average value than normal charting procedures.

The Cusum chart has application in many fields of management control not only quality control. Other areas include:

    Forecasting      -     actual v forecasted sales

    Absenteeism    -     detection of slight changes

    Production levels -     detection of slight changes

    Plant breakdown  -    maintenance performance

As well as many others in which an indication of change is required.

# Variability

## Scope and General Principles

*Scope.* This section introduces the principles of Cusum techniques and includes the preparation, charting, presentation and interpretation of data, with worked examples.

*Fundamental requirements.* The fundamental requirements for Cusum charting are as follows:

i.    The observations should be at least on an interval scale of measurement.

ii.   There should be logical grounds for their being sorted into a sequence for plotting.

These requirements are taken in order. The interval properly requires any given numerical difference between two observations to have the same interpretation throughout the range of the variable. Thus a difference of 0.1 mm between the lengths of two objects has the same meaning whether the objects are woodscrews of length 10.1 mm and 10.0 mm or steel girders of length 10,000.1 mm and 10,000.0 mm although the latter difference may be unimportant. Many arbitrary scales do not have this properly: defect ratings are an example, where perhaps a serious defect scores 10 points, a moderate defect 5 and a minor defect 1. We cannot then interpret this to mean that the following items are necessarily equally undesirable, although their differences are zero.

| | | |
|---|---|---|
| Item A | One serious defect | Score = 10 |
| Item B | Two serious defects | Score = 10 |
| Item C | One moderate, five minor defects | Score = 10 |
| Item D | Ten minor defects | Score = 10 |

Interpretation of 'average' score could be misleading if the balance of major, moderate and minor defects, rather than merely their overall frequency, changes.

# Introduction to Quality

The logical sequences property may arise in numerous ways. Most obviously, the observations may occur in a time or length sequence, thus forming a natural progression. Monitoring for quality or process control provides many cases of this kind.

Secondly, conditions in the environment from which the observations are taken may vary either deliberately or fortuitously. The data thus falls into obvious groups, but the ordering or observations within these groups may not be of any particular importance.

Thirdly, the items themselves may provide a basis for ordering or, more commonly, for grouping. Manufactured components may be segregated according to the identity of the machine from which they are sampled, or on the basis of whether or not they possess specified defects or other attributes.

Fourthly, observations may be ordered according to the value of some auxiliary variable measured on the items. The Cusum then provides a means of presenting or investigating relationships between variables, augmenting a regression or correlation analysis.

This list of possibilities is not exhaustive and any kind of ordering or grouping that uses some structural feature of the observations or the background from which they are taken may provide the basis for the Cusum sequences.

*Types of data amenable to Cusum charting.* Many types of data satisfy the fundamental requirements (a) and (b) and some examples may be useful. Perhaps the most frequent applications of Cusum charts have been in quality control, where observations (e.g. sample means or ranges) are plotted in sequence to provide a continuous assessment of the state of a process. It is sometimes assumed that such observations have to be normally distributed for the application of Cusum charts. This is not the case, although some distribution models may be necessary when setting up the decision rules. However, when using a Cusum chart as a device for effective data presentation, it is not necessary to specify a distribution, nor to require independence between successive observations (again, this condition is important for decision rules, but not for data presentation). Indeed, the Cusum chart may assist in the identification of features such as serial correlation or cyclic behaviour.

# Variability

Thus data involving ranges or sample estimates of standard deviation may be plotted on Cusum charts, as well as sample averages. Counts of defects or defectives are also encountered in quality control and may be monitored by Cusum charts.

Outside the quality control area, many applications arise. The consumption of fuel by transport vehicles, even by private cars, the response of patients to changes in treatment, trials of systems or weapons in which each trial has a success of failure (1 or 0) outcome - all provide data amenable to Cusum charting.

Some forms of indirect data also occur. In setting up a forecasting system, its performance may be monitored by comparing predicted values with actual values when they become available. The validity or adequacy of a mathematical model for an experiment may be assessed by a Cusum of the residual errors. In this instance the various levels of experimental factors will provide the basis for grouping or ordering.

Data in the commercial and administrative areas may also be usefully subjected to Cusum analysis. Monitoring of absence rates and examination for day-of-the-week patterns, assessment of labour turnover, are typical examples. Even where the size of the sample or group, for which such rates are calculated varies, the Cusum chart can be simply modified to accommodate this.

*Purpose of Cusum charting.* Cusum charting has two main purposes, which are related to the way in which the data is collected.

1.  *Monitoring or control.* Values are plotted on the Cusum chart as they occur, with the aim of detecting any change in the nature of the process generating the observations, such as a change in mean or variability.

    Decision rules are necessary to rationalise interpretation of the chart. When an appropriate decision rule so indicates, some action is taken, depending on the nature of the process. Typical actions are as follows:

    (1)   In a quality control application, adjustment of the process conditions.

(2)  In a more general technical context, investigation of the underlying cause of the change.

(3)  In monitoring the behaviour of a forecasting system, analysis of and, if necessary, modification to the model or its parameters.

2.  *Data analysis.*  A complete set of observations is subjected to Cusum analysis, the object being to detect whether changes (e.g. in mean level) have occurred at one or more points in time, or between the rational groups into which the data is divided.  The objectives are close to those of hypothesis testing, except that the group or time-segments into which the data is divided may be based on an examination of the Cusum pattern, instead of being determined in advance as in conventional hypothesis testing.  In essence it is an attempt to detect any changed points in the sequence.

Where historical data, i.e. data collected over time and measuring the past behaviour of systems is involved, the procedure is often termed 'retrospective' or 'post mortem' analysis.  However, as previously noted, grouping by features other than time may often be appropriate.

For either primary purpose, or in intermediate cases, the changes should be assessed against the intrinsic variations in the data.  For time sequences, this means detecting sustained changes in a typical level against a suitable measure of short-term variation.  For other forms of grouping, the problem, such as in analysis of variance, is in comparing between-group variation with the variation within groups.

# Variability

## Case Study

Suppose a liquid chemical were to be prepared, in which the average content of a particular ingredient needed to be as near as possible to 10 g/litre. The liquid produced will be mixed in bulk before the next operation, so minor variations do not matter, so long as the average is kept at 10 g. A cumulative sum chart may be used for this. Start with a reference value, in this case the 10 g/litre, as the basis for controlling the process. This may well be the previous average performance of the process. The process is tested by sampling at intervals The different between the observed sample values and the target reference value is added to the previous value and plotted.

Suppose that the first 10 results are:

| Observation No. | Observed Value = 0 | Deviation from Target (10) | Cumulative Sum of Deviations |
|:---:|:---:|:---:|:---:|
| 1 | 10 | 0 | 0 |
| 2 | 11 | +1 | +1 |
| 3 | 9 | -1 | 0 |
| 4 | 10 | 0 | 0 |
| 5 | 12 | +2 | +2 |
| 6 | 9 | -1 | +1 |
| 7 | 10 | 0 | +1 |
| 8 | 8 | -2 | -1 |
| 9 | 10 | 0 | -1 |
| 10 | 11 | +1 | 0 |
|  | Average = 10 |  |  |

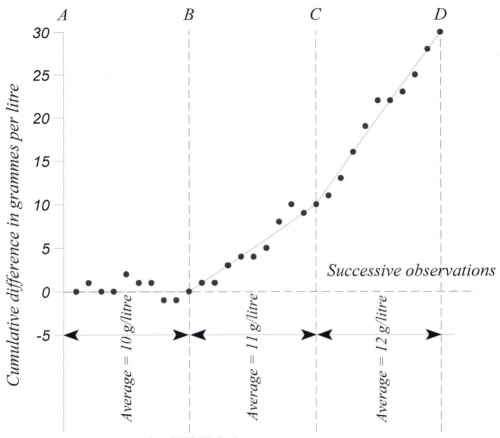

**Figure 118   Example of a CUSUM chart**

These results are plotted in section AB of **Figure 118**.

# Variability

Suppose the observations continue as follows:

| Observation No. | Observed Value = 0 | Deviation from Target (10) | Cumulative Sum of Deviations |
|:---:|:---:|:---:|:---:|
| 11 | 11 | +1 | +1 |
| 12 | 10 | 0 | +1 |
| 13 | 12 | +2 | +3 |
| 14 | 11 | +1 | +4 |
| 15 | 10 | 0 | +4 |
| 16 | 11 | +1 | +5 |
| 17 | 13 | +3 | +8 |
| 18 | 12 | +2 | +10 |
| 19 | 9 | -1 | +9 |
| 20 | 11 | +1 | +10 |
|  | Average = 11 |  |  |

These results plotted in section BC of **Figure 118** form a straight line going upwards and this indicates that the process has changed to a new average level which is higher than the reference value. A check shows that it is averaging 11 g/litre instead of 10. In section CD of **Figure 118** further observations are plotted, in which the average is 12 g/litre.

Interpretation of a Cusum chart is therefore as follows:

1   A horizontal line of points means that the process is holding an average value equal to the reference value.

2   A straight line upwards means that the process has changed to a new steady average level, which is above the reference value. The steeper the line, the greater the difference between the new average and the reference value. (Conversely if the straight line is downwards, the new average is below the reference value.)

3   If the line is curved upwards, the new average is above the reference and still increasing. Similarly, if it is curved downwards, the average is below the reference and still reducing.

4   Notice that the position of a point on the chart represents the cumulative past history of the process since observations were started. Thus there is no particular significance in whether the point is high up or low down on the paper. If points run out of the top of the chart, it is common practice to restart them again near the bottom. All that matters is the direction in which the points are heading. In the above example, the process must be adjusted so that they keep a horizontal course.

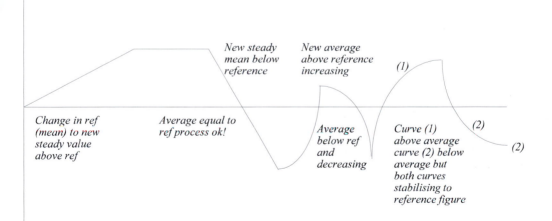

**Figure 119** Interpretation of a Cusum Chart

# Variability

## Scaling factors with cusum charts

The main interest is in the slope of a Cusum plot, the choice of its vertical and horizontal scales will be very important. It can be quite useful to have templates which indicate the expected slope for various quality levels. This may be in the form of attributes or variables as illustrated below.

An example of Cusum charting from lithographic plate process.

## For Attributes

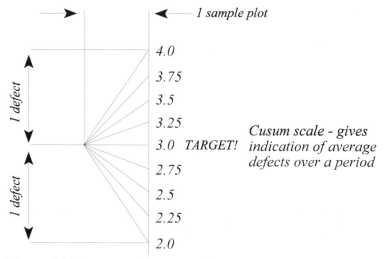

**Figure 120** Cusum attribute template

**Scaling for variable Cusum charts**

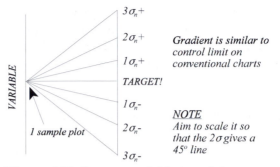

**Figure 121** Custum variable template

**Figure 122** V-Mask for Cusum chart

Point A is placed on the last considered point. If the plotted points fall within the Vee, then the process may be assumed to be under statistical control.

# Addendum

## Glossary of Terms

Below are some definitions which do not appear in the book which have been included for reference.

| Phase | Explanation and Cross reference |
|---|---|
| Accelerated Test | A test which simulates the life of a product over a short period. For example, the expected life of a lawn mower can be simulated within a week of continuous use. See - Prototype Testing. |
| Backward Control | Similar to feedback control. See - modern approach. |
| Bar Chart | Examples in this book are found in Cost of errors and Basic Statistical Methods, e.g. histogram. |
| Bathtub curve | See - Reliability and Patterns of Failure. |
| Cumulative Frequency Curve | When the frequencies of successive class intervals are added the resulting curve is called a Cumulative Frequency Curve |
| Dispatch | See - shipping |
| Forward Control | Similar to backward control except that information found during inspection is fed forward to the next stage to enable compensations to be made for deviations in the previous stage. It is sometime easier or more economic to do this - see modern approach. |
| Goods Inwards Inspection | See - Goods Receiving Inspection |
| In-process Inspection | See - Patrol Inspection |
| Life Test | See - Prototype Testing |
| Limiting Quality | LQ is also called LTPD. See - Lot Tolerance Percent Defective |

| Mean Time to Failure | MTTF is similar to MTBF (Mean Time Between Failures) |
|---|---|

Management Controllable Defects — Defects or random variation that requires management action to resolve. For example, improving the process performance possibly by buying a new machine or changing or widening the process specification or tolerance. See - Common causes of variation.

Normal Inspection — A standard Acceptance Sampling Plan - see also switching rules, tightened inspection and reduced inspection.

Open and Closed Loop — See - Quality Control and modern approach.

Operator Controllable Defects — Defect or non-random causes of variation which can usually be spotted by the operator if they are provided with the correct training regarding interpretation of control charts. See - Data analysis and variation reduction and Special causes.

Performance Indicators — All organisations need to establish and quantify the key factors with which to monitor their quality performance. It is not enough to believe that the organisation's quality performance has always been satisfactory. Agreement needs to be reached as to what the key factors are by which to judge the organisation's quality performance. What is the organisation's current performance against these factors and how can the current quality performance be improved? If measures of Quality Performance are not established and monitored then adverse and possibly catastrophic trends may not be identified with possible dire consequences for the organisation concerned. Juran talks about breakthrough and control to new levels of quality performance; organisations that can achieve this objective will always be successful because they will continually be making never-ending improvements.

Physical Characteristics — Attributes of a product or service. See - Multiple characteristic charts.

Pre-control — See tolerance based control charts.

# Addendum

Process Costing | A method of calculating the cost of quality for processes. See - "Quality Management (Principles & Techniques)" Geoff Vorley. See - Quality costs which describes a method of calculating the cost of quality for organisations.

Psychological Factors | Human errors such as errors of perception, interpretation, judgement etc. - See inspection errors

Screening | Inspecting to filter out defective work. See - traditional approach

Tightened Inspection | See - Switching rules

Truncated test | A reliability test that is halted after sufficient information has been gathered to reach a conclusion. See - Prototype Testing

Viewing | An old term referring to inspection. Also sometimes used to mean visual examination of the finished product. See - Quality Control Strategy

# Introduction to Quality

## IQA D1 - Introduction to Quality Syllabus

Consult the contents list to find reference to each of the following syllabus items:

1    Quality concepts, philosophy and systems

1.1  Establishment and interpretation of an organisation's quality policy

1.2  Natural, material and subjective standards

1.3  The relationship between specifications, measurements and process capability

2    Standardising Organisations

2.1  Company, industrial and national.

2.2  Product Certification procedures

3    Total Involvement in Quality

3.1  Communication and feedback of information.

3.2  Justification of quality assurance activities

3.3  Supplier evaluation rating

4    Quality Costs

4.1  Process Cost Model

4.2  Prevention Appraisal Failure Model

4.3  Taguchi Loss Function.

5    Statistical Process Control

5.1  Process Capability studies

5.2  Statistical Process Control Charts

5.3  Calculation and use of decision lines

6    Reliability

6.1  Basic concepts of series and parallel systems

6.2  Use of redundancy to improve reliability

6.3  Interpretation of time life distribution in terms of probability density function and reliability function


7    Variability

7.1  Continuous and discrete random variables

7.2  Probability distributions

7.3  Binomial and Poisson distributions

7.4  Application of acceptance sampling by attributes

7.5  Construction and interpretation of Operating Characteristic curves

**Index**

# Index

# Index

# Index

# Introduction to Quality